CU00820273

GEOLOGISTS' ASSOCIATION ⌣⌣⌣⌣ ⌐⌐. ⌐⌐

GEOLOGY OF THE DORSET COAST

Second Edition

by MICHAEL R. HOUSE

Edited by C. J. Lister & J. T. Greensmith

1993

GEOLOGY OF THE DORSET COAST

by MICHAEL R. HOUSE

CONTENTS

II SOUTH DORSET COAST

III EAST DORSET COAST

MAPS, MEMOIRS AND OTHER GUIDES

TIDES AND OTHER HAZARDS

PREFACE

The Dorset coast has been a delight for amateur geologists and a training ground for professional geologists for almost two centuries. It is quite unsurpassed in Britain and probably Europe for the variety of post-Palaeozoic sedimentary rocks and their tectonic structure seen in a small compass. It displays better than anywhere those rocks and structures that have been the basis for the search for hydrocarbons in western Europe for the last twenty years.

For the geologist the coast is almost all things to all men, the stratigrapher, sedimentologist, palaeontologist, palaeoecologist, tectonician, engineering geologist and geomorphologist all finding much that formed the basis for classic studies in their disciplines. It will be impossible to please all of them with this guide. However, despite the considerable published work, it is difficult for a geologist to take more than a few paces along the Dorset coast without encountering puzzles and fascinating problems that still require solution.

This guide aims to provide a general introduction to what may be seen, and where. Emphasis is placed on the localities and the precise discrimination of the stratigraphic successions. It is hoped in this way new observations can be better integrated with earlier work and thus form a more scientific basis for individual study, thought, interpretation and argument. Most emphasis is placed on the Jurassic rocks because these are such an international standard. Rather less detail is given on the Cretaceous and Tertiary rocks because these rocks are as well or better seen elsewhere, and the Dorset Chalk cliffs, being mostly vertical, are also dangerous. In any case, with such a wealth of geology to describe, some selection has been essential. The introductory sections on Sedimentology and Palaeontology have been added by request to introduce specialist terms to the general reader.

Because of the ready road access for cars (but rarely coaches) it is expected that users of this guide will arrange their own programmes. There is good connection to the main towns by buses from Weymouth, which is easily reached by train from London. The guide is arranged from west to east, that is roughly from oldest to youngest rocks. It covers the ground of the Dorset Coastal Path. For those with only little time for a visit, the coast west of Lyme Regis (Itinerary 2A), Portland (Itinerary 11), Osmington Mills (Itinerary 12C) and Lulworth (Itinerary 17E) provide especial interest and the splendid Dorset Museum, High Street Dorchester, and Maiden Castle (Itineraries 8D, 8E) should not be neglected.

The author would like to record his thanks to the late W.J. Arkell, whose publications initiated his schoolboy interest in the coast and on whose recommendation he was invited to write an earlier guide (published in 1958 and revised in l969). Professor D.V. Ager is thanked for allowing this guide to extend to the western part of the Dorset coast which was covered by an early guide of his and W. Smith. The cliff profiles and sections have been newly constructed for this guide and all text-figures have been drawn by the author except for four which were redrawn by P. McSherry; the author's negatives for the plates have been printed by M.J. Rastrick; Heather Barnes has prepared the typescript; all are at the University of Hull. Thanks are due to the Editor, Carol Lister, Felicity House, Dr. W.J. Kennedy and P. Ensom for helpful comments on the whole typescript and to Dr W.S. McKerrow, Mr R.P.H. Edmonds, Niall Sharples and Muriel Arber for comments on particular parts. Generations of students have provided thought-provoking, awkward questions and drawn attention to facts which invalidate sweeping generalisations. A fruitful association with Poroperm Laboratories Ltd. and with Dr. M. Ashton and Dr. T. Harland has led to a similar contribution by many exploration geologists, which is gratefully acknowledged.

PREFACE TO SECOND EDITION

The first edition having sold out quickly, and reprints being almost exhausted, a second edition is now offered which corrects some earlier mistakes and is a little expanded, especially with regard to the background to the success of hydrocarbon exploration in the region and modifications due to the publication of a new *Memoir* on the Bournemouth area. I have benefited from helpful comments from Drs I.M. West and J.R. Andrews and of Profs J.M. Hancock and R.M. Carter. Little has been done to meet the criticism of the first edition that the new coastal profiles were reproduced too small — they had been intended as fold outs but that proved too expensive. Enlarging copiers are now available for those that find this a problem. A more fundamental criticism of the first edition was the failure to use a rigid Formation and Member terminology. With so many variants available I chose then, and now, mostly to follow the conservative terminology of the Geological Society's correlation charts. For Member terminology the mere change of a familiar name seems unnecessary and unhelpful, such as a recent proposal to replace the terms Lower, Middle and Upper Oxford Clay, by the Peterborough, Stewartby and Weymouth Members (which ignores a name having priority for the last). Consistent usage by the Geological Survey would be helpful or, better, a national committee to resolve the different usages of the Survey, the petroleum industry and research workers, but these matters are not for an introductory guide such as this. Finally it is a pleasure to record indebtedness to the Petroleum Exploration Society for a grant which allows the inclusion of coloured photographs and to our President, Eric Robinson and Guides Editor, Trevor Greensmith for the constant prodding and interest which finally led to this edition.

1. Itineraries and Localities

2. List of Figures

3. Explanation of Plates

Plate 1: The Lower Lias in Pinhay Bay.

Plate 2: The Lower Lias near Seven Rock Point.

Plate 3: View of the East Dorset coast from Seven Rock Point to beyond Golden Cap.

Plate 4: Thin sections illustrating the fabric of some Liassic rocks.

Figure 5: Coastal views from Golden Cap to Thorncombe Beacon.

Figure 6: The Bridport Sands and overlying rocks in Burton Cliff.

Figure 7: Thin sections and structures in the Bridport Sands at Burton Cliff.

Figure 8: Inferior Oolite at Burton Cliff.

Figure 9: Illustrations of Bridport Sand to Forest Marble.

Figure 10: Views of the Hardy Monument and the Fleet.

Figure 11: The Portland Beds on Portland.

Figure 12: Thin sections showing lithologies of the Portland Beds.

Figure 13: Portland Freestone and Portland ammonites.

Figure 14: Coastal views from Bowleaze Cove to Osmington Mills.

Figure 15: The Corallian Beds near Osmington Mills.

Figure 16: Thin sections showing lithologies of the Corallian Beds.

Figure 17: Thin sections of the Abbotsbury Ironstone, Upper Greensand and Wealden Beds.

Figure 18: Views of the unconformity at White Nothe and trace fossils at Bran Point.

Figure 19: Views around Bat's Head, Durdle Door and Man-o'-War Head.

Figure 20: Views of Stair Hole.

Figure 21: Views of Lulworth Cove.

Figure 22: The Fossil Forest east of Lulworth Cove.

Figure 23: Views of Mupe Rocks and Worbarrow Bay.

Figure 24: Kimmeridge Bay showing structures in the Flats Stone Band.

Figure 25: Views of the Kimmeridge Oil Well and Kimmeridge Bay.

Figure 26: Views from Clavell Hard to White Lias Rocks.

INTRODUCTION

In the late Palaeozoic the Canadian shield, North Europe, Scandinavia and European Russia (west of the Ural Mountains) are thought to have been united in a land mass called Laurussia. In the early Mesozoic, continental breakup of Laurussia began and North America and Europe separated, firstly giving restricted and fault-bounded terrestrial basins in the Triassic, and later a progressively enlarging Atlantic Ocean. The deposits of Dorset should be seen in this broader palaeogeographical setting. At a later stage the marine intercontinental sea corridors of the Jurassic gave way progressively to the more open marine conditions of the late Cretaceous. With the Tertiary, and continental shelf uplift, the record is of coastal margin and strictly terrestrial conditions.

Although Palaeozoic rocks are known in boreholes at depth beneath southern Dorset, only Mesozoic and Tertiary rocks are exposed along the coast. The Triassic crops out on the coast of east Devon where it is unconformably overlain by the Upper Cretaceous, and its boundary with the lowest Jurassic is seen in Pinhay Bay just west of Lyme Regis. The famous and fossiliferous Liassic sections of the Lower Jurassic are best seen along the coast between Lyme Regis and Bridport (Fig. 1a). Middle and Upper Jurassic rocks form broad outcrops in the Weymouth lowlands, on Portland, and in the Isle of Purbeck between Lulworth and Swanage. The best exposures of the Cretaceous are between White Nothe and Worbarrow Bay, and again north of Swanage (Fig. 1a). Tertiary rocks are exposed in Studland Bay and on the cliffs around Bournemouth.

It might be expected from the projection of the axis of the Hercynian Culm Synclinorium of Devon that Upper Carboniferous rocks would form the Hercynian basement to the area. However, boreholes near Cranborne (SU 0340807073), 16km north of Poole, reached ?Upper Devonian at 1663m depth, and a borehole at Wytch Farm (SY 980853), 6.6km south-southwest of Poole, encountered ?Middle-Upper Devonian at 2730m (Colter and Havard 1981). At Nettlecombe (SY 505954), 4.5km north-east of Bridport, Lower Carboniferous was proved below 1904m depth. The Winterborne Kingston borehole (SY 84709796), 20km north-east of Dorchester, was stopped in Permian at 3043m (Rhys *et al.* 1982). At Seaborough (ST 434062), 14km north of Bridport, Carboniferous was thought present below 1554m.

During the Mesozoic, thicker sedimentation occurred in the Purbeck area and most units thin to the west, that is, towards what are inferred to have been land areas in Cornubia during the time of their deposition (a geological map of the pre-Permian floor is given by Sellwood *et al.* 1986).

1

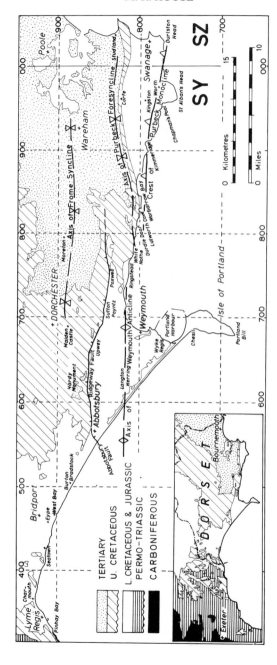

Figure 1.   Geological sketch map of the Dorset coast showing the National Grid which
is used for locality reference throughout the text. a, Geology; b, Localities
and main routes.

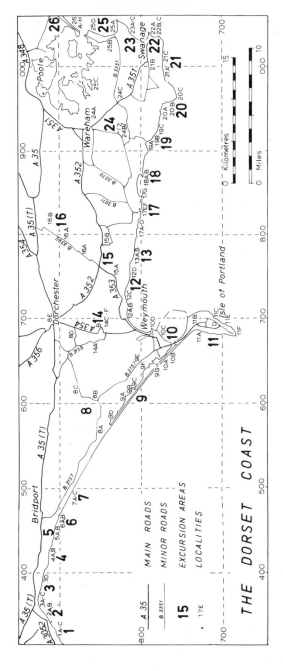

THE DORSET COAST

A major period of tensional earth movements with faulting and folding occurred in the middle Cretaceous (pre-Albian), following Wealden deposition and preceding deposition of Gault and Upper Greensand (Albian) and probably preceding much of the Lower Greensand (Aptian). This is the date of the major unconformity within the Dorset Mesozoic sequence, as a result of which late Cretaceous rocks rest on progressively older rocks to the west (Fig. 1a, inset 2). The Upper Cretaceous rests with minor discontinuity on Lower Cretaceous in east Dorset, and is quite conformable with it in the Isle of Wight. Upper Cretaceous rests unconformably on the Lower Jurassic at Lyme Regis, on Triassic in east Devon and reaches within a few kilometres of the Hercynian granite of Dartmoor near Newton Abbot.

The second major period of folding and faulting to affect the outcropping rocks of Dorset occurred in the early and mid-Tertiary. The effects of this phase are best displayed in south and south-east Dorset. The southern part of the broad arch of the Weymouth Anticline may be of this date, but the most prominent structures are the Frome Syncline and to the south the spectacular north-facing Purbeck Monocline, the middle limb of which is vertical or overturned, as between Bat's Head near White Nothe and Ballard Down.

1. STRATIGRAPHY

The Dorset rock succession is illustrated in Fig. 2. Almost all units thicken towards the south-east where the Jurassic, for example, probably exceeds 1400m in thickness. In the discussion below the thickness of units quoted refers to the maximum known at outcrop : at depth, and especially to the south-east, thicknesses may be considerably greater. Thicknesses of the Jurassic and Cretaceous rocks of Dorset (*ca.* 2.5km), when divided by the time interval involved (73−213 million years), suggest average sedimentation rates of about 0.2mm/year.

There is much variation in the formal lithostratigraphic names given to the Dorset succession. Units such as the Oxford Clay or Corallian are best regarded as formations. The scheme favoured is shown on Tables I−VI (pp. 13 to 18). To avoid a cumbersome formal terminology in both text and diagrams ancient terms, many dating from William Smith himself (1769−1839), are used, a procedure sensibly adapted by the Geological Society of London in their excellent series of correlation reports for the Triassic, Jurassic, Cretaceous and Caenozoic (Warrington *et al.*, 1980, Cope *et al.*, 1980, Rawson *et al.*, 1978, Curry *et al.*, 1978): reference should be made to these for details.

The Triassic is essentially non-marine except that the Rhaetic transgression introduces marine beds near the top. The Jurassic and Cretaceous rocks are almost wholly marine apart from the Purbeck and Wealden Beds which are largely non-marine. Several levels in the early Tertiary are also non-marine; the Upper Tertiary is not represented.

Dominating the Mesozoic and Tertiary sequences of the Dorset coast is a series of major sedimentary rhythms (Fig. 2). These commonly comprise triplets of clay, silt/sand and limestones in succession and in that order. The rhythms

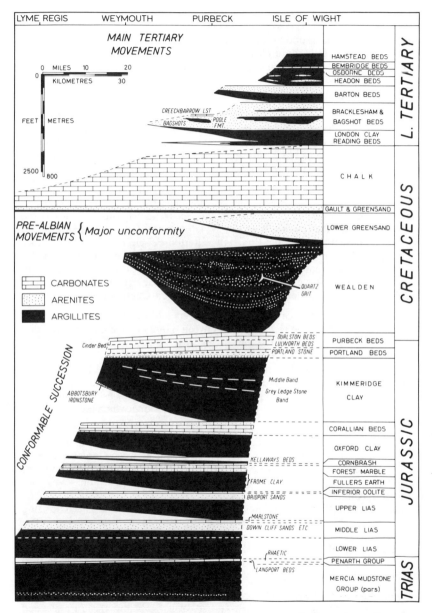

Figure 2.   The Dorset geological succession drawn to emphasise major sedimentary rhythms throughout the succession (after House 1983).

represent shallowing-upward or regressional sequences. Many of these have been regarded as eustatic and due to global changes in sea level. But a local or regional cause related to faulting and to continental break-up associated with the formation of the North Atlantic is more plausible for many. Climatic changes may be the cause of other rhythms particularly those of very small scale.

Triassic (*ca.* 248–213 million years ago)

The Triassic, the upper and Mesozoic part of the New Red Sandstone, is represented in the subsurface by non-marine deposits formed in desert environments with widely spread flood gravels, sands and muds associated with playa-lake environments. At the close of the period marine rocks enter, heralding the transgression of the early Jurassic.

The Trias is exposed on the east Devon coast between Budleigh Salterton and Pinhay Bay west of Lyme Regis. The sequence commences with the Sherwood Sandstones Group (formerly Bunter Pebble Beds and Sandstone). This is the reservoir rock for the lower trap in the Wytch Farm oilfield in east Dorset. On the Devon coast it includes the Budleigh Salterton Pebble Beds (some 21–14m thick) of fluviatile conglomeratic sandstones with Ordovician quartzite pebbles and overlain by current-bedded and aeolian red sandstones. Budleigh Salterton-type large, oval pebbles are known from the high Tertiary gravels in West Dorset and they form a minor constituent of the pebbles on Chesil Beach.

The Mercia Mudstone Group (formerly Keuper Marl, Tea Green and Grey Marls) crops out along the Devon coast between Sidmouth and Culverhole Point east of Seaton. It comprises red and green silty mudstones of playa-lake type with thin sandstones : a thickness of 356m was estimated in the Lyme Regis borehole of 1901 where the sequence contained much gypsum and some halite (Warrington and Scrivener 1980). These evaporites have been held to play a role in the dramatic structures farther east by providing slip surfaces for listric faults at depth. Evaporite levels would give weak horizons along which tectonic movements could be accommodated.

The uppermost Triassic unit, the Penarth Group (formerly middle and upper Rhaetic, White Lias and lowest Blue Lias) crops out between Culverhole Point and Pinhay Bay. The Group reached 18.5m thickness in the Lyme Regis borehole (Warrington and Scrivener 1980). Marine shales comprise the Westbury Formation (Contorta Shales) and these are overlain by a weakly developed Cotham Member (formerly White Lias and lowermost Blue Lias) comprising micritic and algal limestones interpreted as forming in a shallow lagoon. The Triassic/Jurassic boundary is drawn where the ammonite *Psiloceras* enters in the early part of the Blue Lias (Plate 1B, Itinerary 1C) rather than at the striking facies change at the base of the Blue Lias but this is an arbitrary, rather than convenient boundary.

Geophysical exploration and some borehole data indicate that the Triassic rocks lie in east-west trending, rift-faulted troughs below the Jurassic and Cretaceous in mid and eastern Dorset. Chief of these is the Crediton-Wimborne trough which underlies central Dorset. There is also subsurface evidence of north-west to south-east trending faults (Melville and Freshney 1982, Fig. 31) affecting the Triassic, but these do not show at the surface. It is clear from seismic and other data that earlier faults, especially those trending east-west, produced 'highs' above which sedimentation was less than in adjoining more basinal downward-sagging areas, and that these operated throughout the Jurassic and Cretaceous. Such faults which show movement through long periods of sedimentation are termed growth faults.

Jurassic (*ca.* 213–144 million years ago)

The Lower Jurassic or Lias comprises predominantly clays, thin limestones and siltstones. The sequence (Fig. 6) records an initial deepening of the sea followed by two upward shallowing rhythms, the first culminating in the carbonates of the upper Middle Lias (Marlstone Rock Bed) and lower Upper Lias (Junction Bed), the second rhythm terminating with the Middle Jurassic carbonates of the Inferior Oolite (Fig. 6).

The Lower Lias crops out in the cliffs between Pinhay Bay and Seatown. It includes the Blue Lias (Bed H25 and above, 26m, Fig. 9), a series of alternating marine shales and thin limestones suggesting a progressively increasing marine depth. Overlying the Blue Lias are the Shales with Beef (25m), Black Ven Marls (50m, with evidence of non-sequences), Belemnite Marls and Stone (23m) and Green Ammonite Beds (34m). Of these the Belemnite Marls are the most kerogen-rich. The Lias shales are now considered probable source rocks for local oil shows (Stoneley and Selley 1986).

The base of the Middle Lias is taken 3m below the Three Tiers (10m), a marker level of three siltstones seen in the cliffs between Charmouth and Seatown (Fig. 5b). The overlying Eype Clay (66m), Down Cliff Sands (23m) and Thorn-combe Sands (23m) comprise another shallowing upwards rhythm terminating in the Marlstone Rock Bed and Junction Bed (2m) which is a condensed micritic limestone with non-sequences and hardgrounds. The Upper Lias (Toarcian) deepening is seen in the Down Cliff Clay (21m) which is followed by the shoal and storm-sands of the Bridport Sands (45m) (this unit forms the upper trap in the Wytch Farm oilfield).

The Middle Jurassic Inferior Oolite (3–6m) is the first notable limestone in the succession (Fig. 10): it is a condensed sequence of micritic and detrital limestones. The succeeding Fuller's Earth Clay (250m), the lower part called by some the Frome Clay, represents a moderate deepening with shallowing upward into clays and shelly limestones of the Forest Marble (*ca.* 30m) followed by the persistent fossiliferous limestones of the Cornbrash (9m) which is said to be the reservoir and productive level in the Kimmeridge oil well. The overlying Kellaways Beds (*ca.* 15m) comprise a small rhythm of shales followed by sandstones and terminated by the Kellaways Rock, but these rocks rarely exposed.

The base of the Upper Jurassic is drawn within the Oxford Clay (180m) which represents the first major deepening phase since the Lias. The early (Middle Jurassic) part of the Oxford Clay is kerogen-rich. The Nothe Grit (8m) represents transitional sandstones at the base of the Corallian (60m) which is the second major carbonate development of the local Jurassic. The Corallian is divisible into three small-scale rhythms. The facies of oolites and bioclastic limestones is interpreted in the light of the carbonate sediments known at the present day in the Bahamas and other areas (Wilson 1968, 1980). The Kimmeridge Clay (531m) follows which is the thickest clay unit of the local Jurassic. The middle portion of which is highly kerogen-rich: the chief level is the Blackstone or Kimmeridge Oil Shale. The Blackstone represents a deep-water anoxic clay facies. This level in Dorset and in the North Sea is probably a very significant oil source-rock. Above, the Kimmeridge sequence shows a shallowing through dolomitic silts of the Portland Sand to the marine limestones of the Portland Beds (total 73m). The overlying Purbeck Beds (120m) include lacustrine and lagoonal micritic limestones and marls, with evaporites as small rhythms in the lower part, and freshwater red and green clays in the upper part, introducing the colours of the lower Cretaceous Wealden Beds above.

Cretaceous (*ca.* 144–65 million years ago)

There is still dispute over the definition of the base of the Cretaceous (Fig. 2). For some while the boundary was traditionally drawn in England at the top of the Purbeck Beds, and that usage may not accord with the boundary as currently used in the marine successions in southern France and the type Tethys. The Cinder Bed, within the Purbeck Beds, has been interpreted as equivalent to the Ryazanian transgression, and hence marks the base of the Cretaceous as used in Russia. A decision on this boundary has still has to be made by the Commission on Stratigraphy. If the second view is followed, the Durlston Formation (Purbeck Beds above the Cinder Bed, 57m) is to be referred to the Cretaceous.

The Wealden Beds (716m) represent terrestrial deposits formed during a widespread regression of the sea. These are best seen in Worbarrow Bay (Itinerary 18) where they comprise multicoloured sandstones, grits and clays. These are interpreted as representing fluvial and alluvial fan deposits below and estuarine and lagoonal facies above. Later erosion has removed much of the succession to the west and Wealden Beds are last seen near Portesham. All of the Wealden Beds appear to be involved in the intra-Cretaceous (pre-Albian) folding and faulting. Some units, especially the Quartz Grit, cross several of the pre-Albian faults confirming that growth faulting was not significant at least west of Lulworth, whatever may have been happening elsewhere. This refutes the suggestion of contemporaneous local, fault-related erosion and deposition (Stoneley 1982, p. 547, Ensom 1985b).

Marine conditions follow the intra-Cretaceous movements. This is part of a major global series of transgressions (Hancock 1968). Post-Wealden Cretaceous rocks follow the Wealden in normal succession in the southern Isle of Wight and the Isle of Purbeck. However, the Lower Greensand near Swanage (Aptian, 60m) thins rapidly to the north and west as indicated by borehole evidence at Wytch Farm and Winterborne Kingston. The Lower Greensand is overstepped westward by the Gault and Upper Greensand (Albian, 58m) which marks the main transgressive level following the pre-Albian movements. The Albian rapidly cuts down onto lower rocks westward, and rests on Lias in west Dorset, Triassic in east Devon, and Devonian near Dartmoor (Figs. 1a, 2).

The base of the Chalk (405m) is also slightly transgressive, the Chalk Basement Bed younging westward. The Chalk is thought to represent an open-water shelf deposit, with minimal clastics entering the depositional area, apart from clays in the Chalk Marl and Plenus Marl of the Lower Chalk (Cenomanian). The Chalk is largely composed of minute planktonic coccoliths and is a very pure limestone indeed. More shoreward (western) facies of the early part (Cenomanian) are seen in west Dorset as the glauconitic Eggardon Grit and, to the west of Lyme Regis, as the Cenomanian or Beer Head Limestone. The Turonian includes all but the lowest few metres of the Middle Chalk, and the lower part of the Upper Chalk and is usually very nodular. The rock horizons, in which early diagenetic carbonate cements are especially well-developed, are thought to represent shallower-water periods. Within the chalk are other levels at which early cementation occurred: these are called 'hardgrounds'. The Upper Chalk (*ca.* 300m) is best seen between White Nothe and Ballard Down. Maastrichtian rocks are not known at outcrop on land in Dorset, but derived Maastrichtian flints occur as clasts in Tertiary gravels, as at Bincombe, and chalky sediments of this age crop out on the sea floor in the Channel.

Tertiary (65–2 million years ago)

The lower Tertiary sequence (Palaeogene) (Fig. 2) is well developed in east Dorset but there are better developments in the Hampshire Basin to the east (Melville and Freshney 1982). No upper Tertiary (Neogene) is known on the Dorset coast. At Studland (Itinerary 25A) there is an unconformity at the base of the Tertiary which is deposited on the Mucronata Zone of the Upper Chalk. The Tertiary deposits are a mostly non-marine sequence of fluvial sands and gravels but with some clays which form the basis for pottery industries in the Poole area. Marine facies appear in the middle Eocene London Clay Formation. The Bournemouth Group (Bagshot Beds) transgresses across the London Clay and Reading Beds westward along the valley of the Frome (Fig. 1a). In the extreme east there are marine intercalations into fluvial sands, but farther west these progressively give way to gravels, mostly composed of Cretaceous cherts and flints, but including Jurassic clasts. These bear witness to deep erosion and probably tectonic activity early in the Tertiary. The evidence of the Isle of Wight Monocline shows that the major fold period is post Oligocene, and probably Miocene in age.

Quaternary (2 million years to present day)

Little evidence remains of this period. There are spreads of alluvial and fluvial gravels at many heights in Dorset, even capping some of the higher hills. Some of the older spreads may date from early Tertiary erosion surfaces and others from a marine pre-Pliocene surface. Younger levels and spreads result from solifluxion and river terraces. These deposits will have been affected by the Pleistocene Ice Ages. A residual deposit is found on chalk lands which includes material derived from the Chalk which is termed clay-with-flints. True Clay-with-Flints seems restricted to very high chalklands, lower Clay-with-Flints is usually contaminated with sands and water-worn pebbles. Late Pleistocene gravels often have artefacts indicating colonisation by man (Arkell 1947, Palmer 1964).

Structural controls of Sedimentation

There is evidence throughout the Dorset succession to suggest that there were local tectonic controls during sedimentation, possibly related to structural lines at depth. Quite apart from the regional westward thinning, which is taken to be the shoreward direction indicating a positive area in Cornubia, the Mesozoic rocks show significant thickness and facies variations from place to place. It seems likely that east-west lines of weakness which gave the known pre-Albian horst and graben structures, and later the Tertiary fold and fault trends, exerted an influence during sedimentation by producing east-west shoals or positive areas during sedimentation.

One of the most significant of areas showing thinning of units is the Lulworth area (Arkell 1947). Accompanying these variations are facies changes documented for the Upper Greensand by Drummond (1970) who invoked the northwest to southeast Mid Dorset Swell to explain them. The Portland Freestone at Portland and Lulworth is predominantly of oolites whilst equivalent beds to the west northwest are lime muds and to the east-southeast bioclastic calcarenites. Townson (1975) suggested a northeast-southeast swell to explain this. Both these features could be explained by more local east-west structures. In the case of the Lulworth 'high' this might be related to the east-west pre-Albian fault line known at depth below it (Itinerary 17).

In a similar way the local basinal developments, such as that in the Portland and Purbeck Beds of the Friar Waddon area could be explained in terms of local basinal subsidence patterns which are controlled by east-west listric fault movement related to the widening of the Atlantic.

The local east-west normal faults of the pre-Albian may be related to large scale north west to south east trending wrench faults elsewhere, but little of this is well documented.

There is, however, some evidence suggesting contemporaneous fault activity and this is usually indicated by evidence of contemporary erosion during sedimentation. The levels and examples are well defined and may be summarised in stratigraphical order below:

1. *Junction Bed (Lias)*. Jenkyns and Senior (1977, 1991) have described evidence for a minor palaeofaulting in the Eype Mouth area (Itinerary 5B).

2. *Forest Marble*. Lake (1986a) has suggested that faulting of the limestones below the Boueti Bed at Herbury (Itinerary 9C) may indicate contemporary palaeofaulting. However, slight wrench movement of later faults may equally explain his observations.

3. *Kimmeridge Clay*. Ferruginous ooliths in the early part of this unit at Osmington Mills (Itinerary 12C) suggest derivation from an area similar

to that of the contemporaneous Abbotsbury Iron Ore. But this may be explained by the ooliths being occasionally carried into deeper water.

4. *Purbeck Beds*. West and Hooper (1969) have described Portland type cherts in the Unio Beds of the Durlston Formation near Friar Waddon (Itinerary 8B). Lake (1986a) has suggested that vertical breccia pipes in the Purbeck Broken Beds (Itinerary 17, 18) may be synsedimentary; but they are more likely to be associated with post-lithification collapse or brecciation structures. Ensom (1985b) has noted derived specimens of the Kimmeridgian ammonite *Pavlovia* at Worbarrow Tout (Itinerary 18A).

5. *Gault*. The basal conglomerate contains vein quartz and lydites probably derived from the Hercynian basement either directly or indirectly. It is probable that pre-Albian erosion overstepped an earlier pre-Aptian erosion. The contrast between the thick succession of the Lower Greensand at Punfield (Itinerary 23B) contrasts with its apparent absence, other than by possibly by a pebble bed, at Wytch Farm (Colter and Havard 1981) (Itinerary 25C).

6. *Upper Greensand*. Drummond (1970) has invoked intra-Cenomanian faulting to explain the loss of part of the Upper Greensand succession between Lulworth Cove and Worbarrow Bay. This may be related to the east-west pre-Albian fault nearby.

7. *Chalk*. The Chalk Rock at Winterbourne Abbas contains clasts of Upper Greensand which Robbie (1950) used to invoke early movement along the Weymouth anticline and which Falcon and Kent (1960) used to invoke salt tectonics in the Compton Valence area. It seems more likely that all result from erosion associated with movements along the east-west lines of growth faults.

8. *Reading Beds*. At East Lulworth and Morden these are reported to contain chalk flints and Upper Greensand and Portland chert pebbles indicating erosion through the chalk in a neighbouring area (Reid 1896).

9. *Bournemouth Group (Bagshot Beds)*. At Moreton (Itinerary 16A), Bincombe and Blackdown (Itinerary 8C) these contain Purbeck cherts and limestones (Reid 1896) and also flints, Albian cherts and some Palaeozoic material (Plint 1982). Within the Creechbarrow Beds (Itinerary 24B) derived flints occur which have been interpreted (Arkell 1947, Plint 1982) as indicating that the Purbeck Monocline was initiated already in the Eocene.

It is significant that many of the cases of palaeofaulting which have been postulated occur when the facies is shallow. Perhaps at those times growth faults did actually penetrate to the sea floor and most erosion took place then. Stoneley (1982) has argued that the Wealden did not extend north of the Purbeck Disturbance, and Ensom (1985b) has suggested the same for the Purbeck Beds above the Cinder Bed. However, both units occur north of the Purbeck Fold, west of White Nothe, and the Quartz Grit in the Wealden Beds extends right across at least two of the pre-Albian faults between Durdle Door and Osmington showing that the major unconformity must have been formed between the late Wealden and the Albian. It is probably Aptian in age.

Minor Rhythms in Sedimentation

Within the major rhythms which have been described above, and illustrated in Fig. 2, are smaller scale oscillatory patterns of sedimentation, sometimes rhythmic (ie. ABCABC), sometimes cyclic (ie. ABCDCBA), which vary in scale from 20m or so in thickness down to a fraction of a millimetre.

In the Corallian Beds three main rhythms have been recognised and variously interpretated (Talbot 1973, Wilson 1980, Sun 1989) (Itinerary 12). These rhythms are about 20m in thickness and include a clay/sandstone/limestone triplet. These are shallowing upward rhythms. A similar scale of rhythm has been suggested by Wimbledon (1987) for the Kimmeridge Clay and by Townson (1975) for the Portland Beds (Itinerary 11).

On a lesser scale are the cyclic patterns of lithologies seen in the Kimmeridge Clay (Itinerary 19). There the scale for each unit is 1–3m and the facies range from clays to oil shales to coccolith limestones (Downie in House 1969, Wilson 1980). Rather similar scale rhythms have long been known in the Oxford Clay but they are not well illustrated in Dorset. The sabkha-type cycles of the early Purbeck Beds (West 1979) grade from stromatolitic limestones with algal heads through evaporites and limestones to ancient soils (Itinerary 11, 17F, 22): these are best interpreted as shallowing upward rhythms.

At similar scale are the rhythmic alternations of shale and limestone seen in the Blue Lias (Plate 1) where the couplets rarely exceed a couple of metres (Itinerary 1B, 1C). A thin bituminous shale often initiates these and the limestones are full of trace fossils. Of similar period are the cemented/non-cemented levels in the Bridport Sands (Itinerary 7B, 7C) (Plate 6B, 6C) and the bedding discontinuities in limestones such as the Purbeck and Portland Beds (Itinerary 11E) (Plate 11B). Of the many possible interpretations there is some indication of orbitally controlled climatic change being important (House 1985, 1986).

On a much finer scale are the laminations at microscopic scale usually of organic bands of kerogen-rich material separated by poorly organic sediment (Plate 4A). These have been described from the Lias and the Kimmeridge Clay and have been interpreted as indicating annual varves. These require further investigation.

2. BIOSTRATIGRAPHY

The Dorset coast has played a significant part in the establishment of a biostratigraphic scale for the Jurassic, Cretaceous and Lower Tertiary rock succession. Accompanying tables (I–VI) give the standard zones for this sequence. For details see the correlation charts of the Geological Society (Cope et al., 1980, Rawson et al., 1978, and Curry et al., 1978). These form the basis of European correlation of the rock succession and also in many cases of global correlation. Thus the biostratigraphic scale forms the basis for an agreed international correlation. The stages represent larger groups of zones which serve a similar purpose. The zones represent levels represented by particular fossils which are usually found only in the zones. To be useful for international correlation a zonal fossil group has to be readily recognisable, show rapid

STAGES		ZONES	DIVISIONS	THICKNESS in metres
TOARCIAN	UPPER LIAS	*Dumortieria levesquei*	BRIDPORT SANDS (PARS)	43
			DOWN CLIFF CLAY	21
		Grammoceras thouarsense *Haugia variabilis* *Hildoceras bifrons* *Harpoceras falciferum* *Dactylioceras tenuicostatum*	JUNCTION BED	4
PLEINSBACHIAN	MIDDLE LIAS	*Pleuroceras spinatum*	MARLSTONE ROCK BED	0·6
		Amaltheus margaritatus	THORNCOMBE SANDS	27
			MARGARITATUS BEDS	2·3
			DOWN CLIFF SANDS	26
			EYPE CLAY	68
			THREE TIERS	10
		Prodactylioceras davoei	GREEN AMMONITE BEDS	34
		Tragophylloceras ibex	BELEMNITE STONE	0·15
		Uptonia jamesoni	BELEMNITE MARLS	23
SINEMURIAN	LOWER LIAS	*Echioceras raricostatum* *Oxynoticeras oxynotum* *Asteroceras obtusum*	BLACK VEN MARLS	46
		Caenisites turneri	SHALES WITH BEEF	25
		Arnioceras semicostatum *Arietities bucklandi*	BLUE LIAS	32
HETTANGIAN		*Schlotheimia angulata* *Alsatites liasicus* *Psiloceras planorbis*		

TABLE I. Divisions of the Dorset Lower Jurassic giving correlation with international stages and zones and a maximum thickness known at outcrop. Most units thin westwards and are cut out westwards by the Cretaceous unconformity. All zones based on ammonites (see Cope *et al.*, 1981a). For details see text.

evolution, be present in a range of different environmental facies, and be reasonably common. For the Jurassic and Cretaceous the marine ammonites serve this purpose, but they became extinct at the close of the Cretaceous. Non-marine facies, such as the Purbeck and Wealden Beds, are locally correlated using small crustaceans (ostracods). The Tertiary zones given are based on plant spores, and there are other zonations using nannofossils, Foraminifera and other groups.

STAGES		ZONES	DIVISIONS	THICKNESS in metres
JURASSIC — MIDDLE	CALLOVIAN	Quenstedtoceras lamberti	MIDDLE OXFORD CLAY	c.70
		Peltoceras athleta		
		Erymnoceras coronatum	LOWER	c.70
		Kosmoceras jason		
		Sigaloceras calloviense	KELLAWAYS ROCK / CLAY	c.20
		Macrocephalites macrocephalus	UPPER	5·0
			CORNBRASH	
	BATHONIAN	Clydoniceras discus	LOWER	2·1
		Oppelia aspidoides	FOREST MARBLE	75
			FULLER'S EARTH (UPPER OR FROME FORMATION)	38
		Procerites hodsoni	WATTONENSIS BEDS	c.7·6
		Morrisiceras morrisi	FULLER'S EARTH (LOWER)	250
		Tulites subcontractus		
		Procerites progracilis		
		Asphinctites tenuiplicatus		
		Zigzagiceras zigzag	ZIGZAG BED	0·15
	BAJOCIAN	Parkinsonia parkinsoni	INFERIOR OOLITE	6·0
		Strenoceras garantiana		
		Strenoceras subfurcatum		
		Stephanoceras humphriesianum		
		Emileia sauzei		
		Witchellia laeviuscula		
		Hyperlioceras discites		
	AALENIAN	Graphoceras concavum	SCISSUM BEDS	1·3
		Ludwigia murchisonae		
		Leioceras opalinum	BRIDPORT SANDS (PARS)	2·0

TABLE II. Divisions of the Dorset Middle Jurassic giving correlation with international stages and zones and a maximum thickness known at outcrop. Most units thin westwards by the Cretaceous unconformity. All zones based on ammonites (see Cope *et al.*, 1981b). For details see text.

STAGES			ZONES	DIVISIONS		THICKNESS in metres
JURASSIC / UPPER	PORTLANDIAN	TITHONIAN (OR)	Cypridea setina / Cypridea vidrana / Cypridea granulosa / Cypridea dunkeri	PURBECK BEDS (PARS)	LULWORTH BEDS	62
			Titanites (?) oppressus / Titanites anguiformis / Galbanites kerberus / Galbanites okusensis / Glaucolithites glaucolithus / Progalbanites albani	PORTLAND BEDS	PORTLAND STONE	73
					PORTLAND SAND	
	UPPER KIMMERIDGIAN	VOLGIAN	Virgatopavlovia fittoni / Pavlovia rotunda / Pavlovia pallasioides / Pectinatites pectinatus / Pectinatites hudlestoni / Pectinatites wheatleyensis / Pectinatites scitulus / Pectinatites elegans	KIMMERIDGE CLAY	UPPER	242
	(LOWER) KIMMERIDGIAN		Aulacostephanus autissiodorensis / Aulacostephanus eudoxus / Aulacostephanus mutabilis / Rasenia cymadoce / Pictonia baylei		LOWER	c.290
	OXFORDIAN		Amoeboceras rosenkrantzi / Amoeboceras regulare / Amoeboceras serratum / Amoeboceras glosense / Cardioceras tenuiserratum / Cardioceras densiplicatum / Cardioceras cordatum	CORALLIAN BEDS		60
			Quentstedtoceras mariae	OXFORD CLAY UPPER		c.90

TABLE III. Divisions of the Dorset Upper Jurassic giving correlation with international stages and zones and a maximum thickness known at outcrop. Most units thin westwards and are cut out westwards by the Cretaceous unconformity. All zones based on ammonites (see Cope *et al.*, 1981a) except for those of the Purbeck Beds (late Portlandian in the sense of Cope *et al.* (1981a) or early Purbeckian in the sense of Arkell (1947)) which are based on ostracods (Anderson 1985). For details see text.

STAGES		ZONES	DIVISIONS	THICKNESS in metres
CRETACEOUS	APTIAN	*Hypacanthoceras jacobi* *Parahoplites nutfieldiensis* *Cheloniceras martinioides* *Tropaeum bowerbanki* *Deshayesites deshayesi* *Deshayesites forbesi* *Prodeshayesites fissicostatus*	LOWER GREENSAND (PARS)	60
LOWER	"WEALDEN"	*Cypridea valdensis* *Cypridea clavata* *Cypridea marina* *Cypridea tuberculata* *Cypridea dorsispinata* *Cypridea aculeata* *Cypridea paulsgrovensis* *Cypridea brevirostrata*	WEALDEN SHALES WEALDEN BEDS	716
	? RYAZANIAN	*Cypridea setina* *Cypridea vidrana* *Cypridea granulosa*	DURLSTON BEDS CINDER BED	57

TABLE IV. Divisions of the Dorset Early Cretaceous giving correlation with international stages and zones and a maximum thickness known at outcrop. The Gault and Upper Greensand is continuous over the whole area, but beds below are cut out westwards. Wealden ostracod zones are based on Anderson (1985), Aptian and Albian ammonite zones are based on Rawson *et al.* (1978): not all zones have been recognised in the Dorset area. For details see text.

STAGES		ZONES	DIVISIONS			THICKNESS in metres
CRETACEOUS / UPPER — MAASTRICHTIAN		Belemnella occidentalis / Belemnella lanceolata	NOT EXPOSED			
SENONIAN	CAMPANIAN	Belemnitella mucronata / Gonioteuthis quadrata / Offaster pilula	UPPER CHALK		RAMSGATE CHALK	260
SENONIAN	SANTONIAN	Marsupites testudinarius / Uintacrinus socialis / Micraster coranguinum (pars)	UPPER CHALK		RAMSGATE CHALK	260
SENONIAN	CONIACIAN	Micraster coranguinum (pars) / Micraster cortestudinarium	UPPER CHALK		RAMSGATE CHALK	260
TURONIAN		Holaster planus / Terebratulina lata / Inoceramus labiatus	MIDDLE CHALK	SEATON CHALK		41
CENOMANIAN		Sciponoceras gracile / Calycoceras naviculare / Acanthoceras rhotomagense / Mantelliceras mantelli	LOWER CHALK	BEER HEAD LIMESTONE		57
LOWER CRETACEOUS (PARS) — ALBIAN		Stoliczkaia dispar / Mortoniceras inflata	UPPER GREENSAND			60
ALBIAN		Euhoplites lautus / Euhoplites loricatus / Hoplites dentatus	GAULT			12
ALBIAN		Douvilleiceras mammillatum / Leymeriella tardefurcata	LOWER GREENSAND (PARS)			

TABLE V. Divisions of the Dorset Late Cretaceous giving correlation with international stages and zones and a maximum thickness known at outcrop. Cenomanian zones are based on ammonites. Zones above the Cenomanian are based on bivalves, crinoids, echinoids and belemnites. (See Rawson *et al.*, 1978 for discussion.) For details see text.

	STAGES			ZONES	DIVISIONS		THICKNESS in metres
TERTIARY	EOCENE	LATE	BARTONIAN	*Rhombodinium perforatum*	(NOT EXPOSED)		
				P. congregatum			
				Homotryblium variabile	HIGHCLIFF SANDS		c. 10
				Rhombodinium porosum	HENGISTBURY BEDS		20
				Rhombodinium draco			
		MIDDLE	LUTETIAN	*Cyclonephelium intricatum*	BOURNEMOUTH GROUP	BOURNEMOUTH FORMATION	c. 100
				P. arcuatum			
				Pthanoperidinium comatum			
LOWER		EARLY	YPRESIAN	*Pentadinium laticinctum*		POOLE FORMATION	c. 94
				Homotryblium abbreviatum			
				Dracodinium varielongitudum		LONDON CLAY FORMATION	30
				Dracodinium simile			
				Wetziella meckelfeldense			
				Wetziella astra			
	PALAEOCENE (PARS)			*Apectodinium hypercanthum*	READING FORMATION		30
				Ceratiopsis speciosa	(GAP)		

TABLE VI. Divisions of the Dorset Lower Tertiary giving correlation with international stages and zones (based on Aubry *et al.*, 1986, Bujak *et al.*, 1980, Curry *et al.*, 1978) and maximum thicknesses known at outcrop. For details see text. The new Bournemouth *Memoir* (Bristow *et al.*, 1991) uses a Bracklesham Group, comprising the Poole Formation and Branksome Sand (Bournemouth Freshwater and Marine Beds). The Boscombe Sand (upper Bournemouth Formation) and overlying beds up to the base of the Headon Beds they refer to as the Barton Group.

3. PALAEONTOLOGY

Almost all of the Dorset rocks yield fossils, and certain horizons have been celebrated for almost two centuries for the interesting remains they carry. This section is intended to introduce some fossil terminology. The study of fossils, or *palaeontology*, is a scientific discipline which contributes to geology in many ways. Fossils give the best way of dating sedimentary rocks; fossils provide the most reliable way of inferring the conditions of environment or *palaeoecology* of past sedimentary rocks; fossils provide our only real information on the nature of former life on Earth; and fossils provide a unique way in which the evolution of organisms in the past may be studied. It should also be remembered that the hard and soft parts of living organisms in the past, as today, soon decay and are *biodegraded* and destroyed after death. Fossilisation is only possible if entombment in sediment and thus protection occurs *before* this decay has proceeded very far. Therefore fossils are unique and represent only a small fraction of life that formerly lived on earth. They should not be indiscriminately collected and later discarded nor the rocks bearing them idly hammered.

The value of any fossil collected depends on the accurate record of the precise locality and horizon at which it was found. If plastic bags are used to collect specimens then a label should be added at once giving these details, including, for example, both grid reference and local distances from a clear landmark. As soon as the specimen has been washed, cleaned and dried, *both* the fossil and the label should be numbered and, if a collection is being built up, details should be put into a catalogue. In this way no ambiguity is possible on the source of the specimen. Only well-documented material is welcomed by museums and national collections and that is where rare and interesting specimens should be lodged to give access to specialists wishing to study the material.

In order to start to give names to fossils found it is necessary first to be able to recognise the group of animals to which they belonged. For Dorset the best start is the slim volumes *British Mesozoic Fossils* and *British Caenozoic Fossils* published by the British Museum (Natural History). Many of the fossils mentioned in this guide are illustrated in these publications. Many common fossils are also illustrated in the British Geological Survey volume *The Hampshire Basin* (Melville and Freshney 1982). The *Atlas of Invertebrate Macrofossils* (Ed. J.W. Murray, 1985) published by Longman is also useful and also covers Palaeozoic fossils.

Fossils are named using the binomial system introduced by Linnaeus so have generic and specific names, as in *Homo sapiens*. Since many more fossil species have been described than genera, assignment to a genus is easiest. Usually a specialist is needed to give a reliable specific name. For determinations at any level it is a great help to visit museums where there are good named collections on display, as in the Dorset County Museum, Dorchester (Itinerary 8E) and in the displays at the Geological Museum, Exhibition Road, London and the British Museum (Natural History), Cromwell Road, London.

Many monographs and papers have been written on particular Dorset faunas. Some of these are referred to in the text and Public Libraries can obtain these through the inter-library loan system if a good geological library is not near. The monographs published by the Palaeontographical Society include detailed descriptions and illustrations of British fossils. The national Palaeontological Association publishes the journal *Palaeontology* which, whilst international in scope, has included many papers on Dorset fossils as will be seen from the references. There is a good review of palaeontological literature referring to Dorset localities given by Macfadyen (1970).

Microfossils are abundant in most Dorset rocks. They are most readily extracted from soft clays and marls by boiling gently in water with a little sodium bicarbonate or detergent (or for hard shales after drying and soaking in paraffin for a few days) and then sieving; a fine coffee strainer or fine metal gauze can be used. A professional sieve of 63 micron size is the most useful. If the residue is washed into a glass bowl and water added it can be 'panned' with water to remove fine clay minerals and if the cleaned residue is brushed onto blotting or filter paper it can be dried in an airing cupboard or very gentle oven. Keep the resulting material in small labelled bottles. Examination under a binocular microscope will enable interesting specimens to be placed in labelled microscope slides which have a 'well' in them. The very rich microfossil faunas of Dorset are listed in a special guide (Lord and Bown (Eds) 1987) which also gives literature references.

All the major animal and plant groups are represented by fossils in the Dorset succession excluding of course, groups which became extinct in the Palaeozoic, especially at the major extinction event at the close of the Permian. The main groups represented are as follows. All have calcareous hard parts unless other-wise stated:

Invertebrates

Foraminifera. These microfossils are usually a millimetre or less in size and occur in Mesozoic and Tertiary marine clays abundantly. They usually consist of chambers which may be arranged as linear or alternating rows or as spirals. Most are bottom dwelling but by the late Cretaceous pelagic groups become important. Giant forams occurs at several levels. *Nummulites* is one of these and occurs in the lower Tertiary (Itinerary 26H). Modern forams can be collected by sieving and washing the scum at high tide lines on sandy Dorset beaches.

Porifera. Bottom-living marine sponges usually disintegrate into their component spicules after death and hence are mostly seen in thin sections of rocks (Plate 12C). The spicules may be of silica, calcite or spongin. The clionid sponges are borers and evidence of these is found as small holes on the surface of fossil shells.

Coelenterates. The commonest fossils of this group are the shallow-water marine corals. They may be simple, with a calyx for only one polyp, or compound with many polyps. In the Dorset these occur, for example in the Boueti Bed (Fig. 10), Ringstead Coral Bed (Bed 25, Fig. 20, Itinerary 12D) and rarely in the Portland Beds (where *Isastraea* is known in Portland Star Agate).

Echinoderms: crinoids. Fossil of bottom dwelling marine sea-lilies usually disintegrate after death into their component ossicles of crystalline calcite. Such debris forms crinoidal limestones and *Pentacrinites* is not uncommon at many levels in the Jurassic for example, in detrital organic limestones of the Forest Marble (Plate 9C) where complete calices of *Apiocrinus* also occur. The pelagic crinoid *Saccocoma* occurs in the Kimmeridge Clay (Itinerary 19C) and in the Upper Chalk *Marsupites* is a guide fossil.

Echinoderms: asterozoans. The marine starfish and brittle stars are not common fossils except at certain horizons such as one level in the Upper Lias (Itinerary 4B).

Echinoderms: echinoids. Radially symmetrical or 'regular' sea urchins are common marine sea floor dwellers and their long spines are often found loose. In the early Jurassic burrowing sea urchins appeared with much smaller spines and are bilaterally symmetrical or 'irregular'. These occur in calcareous beds at many levels but *Micraster* from the Upper Chalk is the commonest example.

Bryozoa. These comprise mostly marine forms with small polyp chambers. Some are minute and lived attached to shells as commonly seen attached to Jurassic brachiopod valves, especially in the Boueti Bed. Others are larger and leaf-like and recognisable by the multipored surface. Fragments may form nuclei to ooliths (Plate 12A).

Annelida. The tissues of worms decay rapidly but their burrowing tubes are often preserved, especially in sandstones and some limestones. Trace fossils such as the U-shaped *Arenicolites* and *Diplocraterion* (seen in the Corallian, Itinerary 12B, 12C etc) and *Rhizocorallium* were probably produced by these.

Arthropoda. These are generally vagrant bottom dwellers living in marine and non-marine waters. Crab and lobster remains are known but are rare. The common trace fossil *Thalassinoides* (Plate 2B) is thought to be a shrimp burrow. The small crustacean ostracods (usually less than a millimetre in size) are common in calcareous shales (Plate 29A) and can readily be extracted from marls of the Purbeck Beds using the technique given above: the genus *Cypridea* with a hooked anterior end is used as a zonal guide and can be recognised with a hand lens in the Purbeck Beds (Itinerary 22A). Insects are usually very rare. Elytra and wings are not uncommon in white chalky micrites of the Purbeck Beds (Itinerary 15A, 22A). The Stonebarrow Flatstone of the Lower Lias has a celebrated fauna (Itinerary 3C).

Brachiopods. The marine lamp shells are common in rather calcareous shallow-water environments. They have two laterally symmetrical valves and are attached to the sea floor by a stalk (pedicle) through an opening in the pedicle valve. Rhynchonellids have coarse-ribbed valves and occur in groups or nests in Blue Lias limestones (Itinerary 2A), commonly in the Brachiopod Beds (Itineraries 5B, 6A), Boueti Bed (Itineraries 6A, 7C, 9C) and Lower Cornbrash (Itinerary 9D) and there is a curiously asymmetric form, *Torquirhynchia inconstans* known from the top of the Corallian (Itinerary 12D). Rather more widespread are the terebratulids which generally have non-ribbed valves. These are common at many levels in the Jurassic and Cretaceous. Inarticulate brachiopods (without teeth) include lingulids which are common in estuarine and deeper-water clayey environments.

Mollusca: gastropods. Snails are common in both marine and fresh water calcareous and sandy deposits. They include burrowers into the sea floor (*endobenthos*) as well as surface dwellers on the sea floor (*epibenthos*). Good non-marine localities include the Purbeck Marble (*Viviparus*, Plate 29C) and Cherty Freshwater Beds (both Itinerary 22A). Marine gastropods are very common at most rather calcareous levels. Particularly well-known is the 'Portland Screw' *Aptyxiella portlandica* (Itinerary 11D).

Mollusca: bivalves. These are common at all levels. The axis of symmetry of valves is the opposite of that in brachiopods and valves are referred to as left or right in relation to the dorsal hinge line. The freshwater mussel *Unio* is common at certain levels in the Purbeck and Wealden Beds (Itineraries 22 and 17G); *Unio* lives mostly within sediment. In shallow waters of low to normal salinity oysters are common in which the left valve is usually attached and the shell composed of lamellar calcite. In typical *Ostrea* and *Praeexogyra* both valves are rather similar and flat: oyster beds of the latter occur in the Fuller's Earth (Itinerary 9B) and Purbeck Cinder Bed (Itineraries 15B, 22A). The small *Nanogyra* shows twisting of the apical part of the shell (oyster banks seen on Itinerary 14D) and twisting is even more developed in the larger *Exogyra* seen at most localities of the Upper Greensand (Itinerary 17A especially). In *Gryphaea*, the 'giant's toe nail', the left valve increased in size and became incurved and this genus occurs especially in the Blue Lias (Itinerary 2A) and Oxford Clay (Itineraries 9I, 12A): this is thought to be an evolutionary adaptation to raise the gap between the valves above muds of the sea floor. In *Lopha* the valves developed zig-zig folding: the genus is common in the Cornbrash and Corallian Beds.

Many marine bivalves lived burrowed in sediment and this shows by a 'gape' between the valves at the posterior end where the siphons protruded. The 4 cm long *Pleuromya* is of this sort and is very often found in life position in rather grey silty beds. Larger forms such as *Pholadomya* and *Goniomya* are common, especially in the Lower Cornbrash (Itinerary 9D). Others such as *Gervillella* (Itinerary 10C) were partially held in sediment by byssal threads. The common Chalk zone fossil *Inoceramus labiatus* probably lived similarly but the larger species from higher in the Chalk probably did so only in early stages.

The scallops, or pectinaceans, are commonly free-living; some even clap their valves to swim nektonically. They commonly have a notch below the right 'ear' indicating attachment by byssal threads in the young but some are attached in this way throughout life. These groups are common in near shore facies throughout the sequence. The noded thick trigoniid shells of *Myophorella* and *Laevitrigonia* are common in Upper Jurassic limestones and the ribbed *Pterotrigonia* occurs in the Upper Greensand: these are relatives of *Trigonia*, a modern shell which leaps actively through the water using a fleshy 'foot'.

Molluscs: ammonites. These typically have a single coiled shell or phragmocone divided by frilled septa into chambers: the animal with tentacles lived in the outermost body chamber. They are very common throughout the succession in marine rocks of the Jurassic and Cretaceous (at the close of which they became extinct) but are less common in the sandstones. Often at a single horizon pairs of large *macroconchs* and small *microconchs* occur which suggest sexual dimorphism: the males might be the smaller. The evolution of ammonites is very complex and this has been used to establish the most useful biostratigraphy internationally. Several reviews of the group have been published (Kennedy and Cobban 1976, Lehmann 1976, House and Senior (Eds) 1981). In the Cretaceous several bizarre coiling patterns occur in the *heteromorph* ammonites as shown by spiral *Turrilites* and hooked *Scaphites* which are found in the Chalk Basement Bed at many Dorset localities.

Molluscs: nautiloids. These have a coiled shell like ammonites but tend to be stouter and do not have frilled septa. *Nautilus* lives today especially in the Phillipines and surrounding areas. Remains are not uncommon in Dorset, especially in the Lias, Nothe Grit and lower part of the Upper Greensand.

Mollusca: belemnites. The bullet-shaped guard of belemnites forms on a short chambered phragmocone indicating an internal shell in contrast to other molluscs. They are common in most rather shallow-water shales in the Mesozoic, particularly in the Belemnite Marls (Itinerary 4A), Oxford Clay and Gault. *Actinocamax plenus* is common in the upper Lower Chalk, and the uppermost Chalk is called the 'Belemnite Chalk' because it is zoned using the group.

Vertebrates

Fish. Complete fish are rare finds although many have been found especially in the Lower Lias and the Purbeck Beds. The common forms are 'ganoid' fish with polished stud-like scales. The scales are not uncommonly washed out of clay or marl residues.

Reptiles. Many remains of extinct reptile groups have been found in the main clay levels of the Jurassic and Cretaceous, especially levels which indicate low-oxygen conditions where little biodegradation has occured. Occurrences have been reviewed by Delair (1958–1960). Marine reptiles include the short headed ichthyosaurs which can reach 10m in length, and long-necked plesiosaurs which are known from the Lower Lias especially and higher Jurassic clays but which become rare in the Cretaceous. The Dorset Lower Lias finds are in many international museums and rival the faunas from Upper Lias horizons at Holzmaden in southern Germany. The Kimmeridge Clay has also produced good faunas (Itinerary 19C). Remains of the ruling land reptiles are rarer and mostly fragmentary bones derived from corpses washed out to sea, but footprints are well known from the Purbeck Beds (Delair 1960, 1982) (Itinerary 22A). Turtles occur especially in the Purbeck Beds. Flying or gliding reptiles are known: the Dorset Lower Lias pterodactyloids are especially famous and in the late Jurassic and Cretaceous pteranodon remains occur very rarely. The separated bones of flying forms can be identified by their delicacy and hollowness; land is unlikely to have been far away.

Mammals. Although minute mammalian teeth are known from late Triassic infills in the Carboniferous Limestone of the Mendips they are exceedingly rare in Dorset apart from the Mammal Bed level of the Purbeck Beds (Itinerary 22A). From the Mammal Bed small teeth and jaws are known of several groups (Clements 1963, Macfadyen 1970). Mammals generally become far more abundant in the Tertiary after the extinction of major reptile groups at the close of the Cretaceous but records are sparse in the Dorset rocks. The richest Tertiary level in Dorset is the Creechbarrow Limestone (Itinerary 24B, Hooker 1986).

Plants

Plant remains generally occur as carbonaceous films or as lignite in shallow water sand or calcareous facies and identification is difficult. At levels where original woody tissue has been silicified then quite excellent preservation of even cell structure is possible (Francis 1983). Palynology is the study of plant spores and good floras of these are known throughout the succession (Lord and Bown (Eds) 1987). The commoner plant groups found fossil are as follows.

Algae. This diverse group includes the coccoliths (Plate 27B) and coccospheres which belong to the Chrysomonadales and range in size from 1–13 microns so are only easily seen under the electron microscope. They are the most important constituent of the Chalk and some Jurassic limestones (Itinerary 19B). The stoneworts, or Charales, are small shrub-like algae incorporating calcareous material in the cells which are common in freshwater deposits in the Purbeck Beds (Plate 29B, Itinerary 22A). The Purbeck Charales were monographed by Harris (1939). Blue-green algae often form algal biscuits and stromatolites (Plate 8B). These are seen in the White Lias (Itinerary 1A), Inferior Oolite (the snuff-boxes, Itinerary 7A, 7B) and Purbeck Beds (Itineraries 11D, 17F) and lamination which is probably of algal origin is often seen in fine-grained limestones. Formerly many trace fossils were called 'fucoids' meaning seaweed-like (after the common genus of brown algae *Fucus*) but it is now recognised that they are mostly animal burrows.

Filicales. Fragments of ferns are known at several levels in the Jurassic. They have been well described from the Wealden Beds of Worbarrow Bay and north of Swanage (Oldham 1976) and are also well known from the plant beds of the Bournemouth area (Itinerary 26C–G).

Gymnosperms. This large group includes the Mesozoic pteridosperms (seed-bearing plants with fern-like foliage) fragments of which can occur in fine siltstones and some clays. The Bennettitales are well represented in the Purbeck Beds by the short-trunked tree *Cycadeoidea* (known as fossil birds' nests to the Portland quarrymen). The conifers are also well represented, the best known being *Protocupressinoxylon*: an introduction to these for the Purbeck beds is given by Francis (1983), for the Wealden Beds by Oldham (1976) and for the Tertiary by Chandler (1962, 1963).

Angiosperms. The flowering plants are poorly known as fossils until the mid-Cretaceous but late Cretaceous facies in Dorset are not appropriate for their preservation. The record in the Tertiary is however very good, especially in the clays of the Poole Formation (Itinerary 24C, 25) and the Bournemouth Group (Itineraries 26C–G). Floras have been well illustrated by Chandler (1962, 1963) and Collinson (1983).

Life Habits of Fossils

Evolution has resulted in most organisms becoming restricted to particular habitats. The major such *niches* are land (terrestrial), sea (marine) and air (aerial). Land habitats are referred to particular places such as rivers (riverine), lakes (lacustrine), marsh, desert and so on. In these places organisms will have certain roles, for example, animals may be herbivores, omnivores or carnivores. In the case of those living in water they may feed on particles as *deposit feeders* (eating particles from the sea floor) or *suspension feeders* (using a filtering system to select food particles). Plants may be xerophytic or hydrophytic according to their water level preference. All can be considered in relation to the food chain of which they formed a part and such *trophic analysis* is helpful. These things form a helpful basis for establishing the nature of past communities and environments.

In marine waters the *benthos* are those organisms living on the sea floor. If they live burrowed (mostly) in the sediment they are *endobenthos*, if on the surface, *epibenthos* (epifauna or epiflora). Some organisms are *fixed* or *sessile*, others are *mobile* or *free-living*. In the past, as today, communities vary much from place to place. The *nekton* comprise free-moving and swimming organisms that can move in the water column although many may prefer habitats close to the sea floor (the *nektobenthos*). Organisms which can tolerate a wide range of salinity are termed *euryhaline* and those which are limited to a narrow range are termed *stenohaline*.

The *plankton* are the floating organisms which drift according with currents. These mostly comprise *microplankton* which may be plant or animal. Many organisms which live as benthos or nekton in the adult stages spent a larval stage in the plankton. *Pelagic* organisms are those which live in ocean areas not necessarily in the plankton. Some plankton have the ability to move up and down in the water column. Plant plankton form an important first step in the food chain for they can holotrophically build up sugars from sunlight. Animal plankton feed on them. At death their remains drop slowly to the sea floor but they will be accompanied by much microfaecal material and most will have passed through several cycles of digestion and defaecation by other organisms.

It is important with fossils to determine whether they are found in sediment in the place where they lived and hence form an association similar to that in life called a *biocoenosis* or whether they were carried into the place where they were fossilised and hence form a death assemblage or *thanatocoenosis*. Clearly interpretation of conditions of formation of a sediment using fossils must use the fossils known to be part of the biocoenosis.

4. SEDIMENTOLOGY

The Dorset rocks are wholly sedimentary in origin. Metamorphic and igneous rocks are not seen except as pebbles or fragments derived from other areas, for example in the river gravels of the Tertiary in the east of the county or in the Portland Raised Beach deposits. In these cases the sediments accumulated in river and beach environments respectively and the fragments came from other areas. The nature and fabric of sedimentary rocks give an indication of how the original sediments were formed and of their origin and the cementation processes or *diagenesis* which led to their lithification. Thus when used in conjunction with fossil evidence, sedimentology becomes an important key for determining past environments. An illustrated introduction is given in the *Atlas of Sedimentary rocks under the Microscope* by A.E. Adams, W.S. MacKenzie and C. Guilford published by Longman. This section aims to provide a guide to some of the terms used to describe sedimentary rocks and sedimentary environments.

There are several terminologies for sedimentary rocks which are built up from aspects of grain size, the degree of sorting of grains, dominant chemical composition and the fabric of the rock. Most of these can be determined with a hand lens. Microscope work uses thin sections and these can be made without too much equipment although an electric rock saw and grinder quickens the process. If a rock fragment 2−3cm across has one surface flattened with a metal file this surface can be polished using progressively finer grades of abrasive corundum powder (sizes 400, 800, 1200 microns) mixed with water to a paste on separate small sheets of plate glass. The polished rock surface is cleaned, dried and glued onto the centre of a 3 × 1 inch glass slide using cold-setting epoxy resin or Canada Balsam (Lakeside 70C) heated on the slide to 85° using a hot plate. When thoroughly cold the lump can be ground down using a file or grinder to an even 0.5mm thickness and then ground down using successive carborundum powders as thinly and evenly as possible the process being watched under the microscope. The ideal final thickness is 0.2mm. After cleaning a thin glass cover slip is glued onto the newly-polished surface. Surplus cement is cleaned off using white spirit and labels giving exact locality and horizon pasted onto the slide. Such slides can be often used as negatives for making photographic prints. Alternatively polished surfaces can be etched in 10% hydrochloric acid for a few second. Then, for small areas, collodian (or nail polish) can be poured onto the surface and peeled off when very dry; when taped between glass slides these can be used for microscope examination. Larger polished surfaces should be dipped in acetone and lightly pressed on acetate sheet in an open space and allowed to dry thoroughly before peeling off and setting between glass plates. The replication by these methods can be extremely good.

Terminology for sedimentary rocks is built up from attributes of the texture and fabric of the rock material. This will be briefly outlined.

Siliceous Rocks

Quartz (SiO_2) is a common resistant mineral in igneous and metamorphic rocks from which many sediments are derived. Quartz cannot be bitten by teeth, cannot be scratched with a knife, and does not effervesce in dilute (10%) hydrochloric acid. Many sedimentary rocks are composed of fragments or *clasts* of quartz and silicate minerals, including aluminosilicates. In the types listed below silicate minerals are most important and these comprise *siliciclastic* deposits. Clast size forms a convenient classification·

Diameter in mm	Unconsolidated (Unlithified or loose)	Consolidated (Lithified or indurated)	General Terms
<0.0039	*clay*	*claystone*	*mudstone*
			argillite
0.0039 – 0.0625	*silt (fine, medium, coarse)*	*siltstone*	*lutite*
0.0065 – 2.0	*sand (fine, medium, coarse)*	*sandstone* *arenite*	
2.0+	*gravel (granules, pebbles, cobbles, boulders)*	*gravel* *rudite* *conglomerate* *(clasts rounded)* *breccias* *(clasts angular)*	

Obviously the grain size tells something of the strength of water currents required for moving the fragments for these will be deposited when the strength drops below a critical value. When all grains are nearly the same size it is said to be *well sorted*; this too tells something of the nature of the history of the sediments. The degree of *roundness* or *angularity* also indicates something of the history: in terrestrial regimes scree fragments are angular and they become progressively more rounded if moved by running water especially under flowing water of *fluvial conditions*. Most beach material is well rounded under the influence of wave action. Wind blown *aeolian* sand grains are extremely well rounded because frictional abrasion is very high.

Further classification is given by the cementing materials which have bound the originally soft sediments during lithification or *diagenesis*. Cementing minerals may be of calcite giving, for example, *calcareous sandstone*, or of iron minerals, giving *ferruginous sandstones*. Other epithets can refer to other attributes, hence *micaceous sandstones* which have common mica flakes (Plate 7B), shelly sandstones which have shell fragments and so on. *Glauconitic* sandstones have the alumino-silicate mineral glauconite and the Upper Greensand illustrates this type.

A considerable range of depositional environments is possible for siliciclastic rocks from scree slopes on land or fluvial deposits in river systems, deltas and estuaries to marine beach deposits with finer grade material being deposited well offshore. The character of the depositional environment is indicated by the bedding patterns seen on a large scale (Plate 6C) or on the smaller scale of current bedding, ripple markings and mud cracks (Itinerary 22, for example).

Rather separate are rocks in which the silica is concentrated after deposition, during *diagenesis*. The *flints*, *lydites* and *cherts* are included here and they develop by the concentration of silica scattered in the rock into nodules (as in the Chalk) or as other shapes. The origin of the silica has been much debated. Some certainly derives from siliceous sponge spicules but some may result from contemporary volcanicity and an increase of silica in sea water which resulted in primary precipitation on the sea floor. Silica can also replace calcitic material of shells, as in the Cherty Freshwater Bed (Itinerary 22A) or woody material of plants as in the Fossil Forest (Itinerary 17F).

Calcareous Rocks

Limestones are composed almost wholly of calcium carbonate ($CaCO_3$) which is easily scratched with a knife, can be easily bitten by the teeth and which effervesces in 10% hydrochloric acid. There are two common calcium carbonate minerals, *aragonite* and *calcite*. The first is commonly preserved in clays of the Lias, Oxford Clay and Kimmeridge Clay but is unstable and usually changes to calcite (the process known as *neomorphism*). Aragonite is probably precipitated from warm waters supersaturated with $CaCO_3$. Organisms can secrete both materials. Dolomites are composed of the double carbonate ($CaCO_3.MgCO_3$) and these may form primarily on the sea or lake floor or may result from neomorphism of calcite by secondary enrichment in magnesium. There is a bewildering range of terminologies for limestones and the ones discussed below should be regarded as means of precisely describing the rock being examined: this forms the first step towards attempting to deduce the environment of formation of the original sediment.

Classification of limestones using grain sizes gives the terms *calcilutites*, *calcarenites*, and *calcirudites* which use the same size criteria as for siliciclastic rocks given in the table above. Intermediates can be referred to as, for example, *calcareous mudstones* or *calcareous sandstones* and, in these, the calcareous element is usually in the binding cement.

The clasts of limestones enable further subdivision. Clasts of broken shell fragments (*bioclasts*) derived from other areas will probably not have travelled far since calcareous materials are not as hard as quartz: usually such clasts are composed of broken fragments of shells and skeletons of organisms living near by. Hence the compound terms like *bioclastic limestone, biomicrite* or *shelly calcarenite*. Bioclasts may include small unbroken fossils or actual microfossils and dominance of the organism can give names such as *coccolith limestone* (Plate 27B) or *ostracod limestone* (Plate 29A). A rock full of shells is often called a *lumachelle* or *coquina*.

In addition limestones often include structures which have developed on the sediment surface, often by concentric accretion of $CaCO_3$ by the action of blue-green algae (Cyanobacteria) or bacteria. The group name for these is *ooids*. Single grains are *ooids* or *ooliths*. Strictly oolites have grains of fish-roe size and grade up to *pisolites* (pea size) or *oncolites* (egg size): larger structures are termed *stromatolites* (Plate 8A,B). When deposited around a nucleus such as a quartz grain (Plate 16A,B) or organic fragment (Plate 12A) the term *superficial oolite* is used. Faecal pellets may be abundant enough to form *pellet limestones*. The term *peloid* is used generally for grains of micritic material some of which may be pellets. The term *intraclast* is used for clasts which are neither bioclasts, ooids or peloids.

Compositional classification of limestones takes into account three elements: the clasts, particles and grains (termed *allochems*). The primary matrix material may be micritic, or may be a later matrix of crystals or *spar* which fill spaces in the primary sediment. Thus a bioclastic limestone cemented by crystals is a *biosparite* (Plate 12B, 29C) but if the matrix is micritic it is a *biomicrite* (Plate 4C, 12C). An oolite with a cement of crystals is a *oosparite* (Plate 12A) and so on. Terms can be compounded as in *bio-oosparite*.

A textural classification recognises *grainstones*, where grains have very little or no original matrix (Plate 22A), *packstones*, where grains are in contact and there is a matrix (Plate 12A), *wackestone* where coarse grains 'float' in a matrix (Plate 4C): *floatstones* may show small (Plate 4C) or large (Plate 8A) 'grains'. In this textural classification a *mudstone* is a micrite with very few larger grains.

Recognition of the particular characteristics of limestones is especially important because it enables deductions to be made on their environment of formation. On land limestones form at calcareous springs giving *tufas* or *sinters*. In calcareous lakes calcilutites, biomicrites and biosparites can form but the fossils will be the main way in which the salinity can be determined. Bioclastic limestones characterise wave-action zones where shells can be fragmented. Oolites form in offshore or lagoonal shallow-shelf areas where gentle rolling of grains on the sea floor enables concentric precipitation of ooids to occur. Coccolith limestones formed from skeletons of planktonic micro-organisms indicate more open-sea environments.

Ferriferous Rocks

The accumulation of iron on land today is mainly in the form of iron oxides such as *hematite*, *goethite* or *limonite*, or the ferrous carbonate, *siderite*. These also occur in marine situations where the iron-rich silicate minerals *glauconite*, *chamosite* and *greenalite* are important. The iron sulphides *pyrite* and *marcasite* form in reducing situations within sea-floor muds. In the Dorset succession sandstones usually have a yellow to brown colour because of the oxidation of iron minerals although when fresh the rock may have other colours: the Upper Greensand which is rich in glauconite, is blue or green when fresh.

Ironstones are only found at few levels. The Marlstone Rock Band (Itinerary 5A, Plate 4C) is rich in iron but it is only the Abbotsbury Ironstone (Itinerary 8A) which has been exploited in the past as an ore, but the venture was unsuccessful because a high silica content (mostly as nuclei grains to the ooliths, Plate 17A) made extraction uneconomical: in this case the iron is in the form of *chamosite oolite* with *siderite mudstone* giving the typical *minette* type of sedimentary ironstone. *Sideritic concretions* are found in the Lias and other levels.

Phosphatic Rocks

The main source of sedimentary phosphates is animal tissue, skeletal and faecal material. Thus bone beds are rich in phosphate. But phosphates can migrate in rocks diagenetically to form *phosphatic nodules* and these may have been concentrated by water action. Usually the mineral is in the form of *collophane* and this gives a chocolate-brown colour to altered rocks. The lowest levels of the Chalk shows phosphatic nodule beds near Swanage (Itinerary 23B) and phosphatic nodules and phosphatised fossils are common in the Chalk Basement Bed as, for example, at Durdle Cove (Itinerary 17A). The basal pebble bed of the Gault also has small, rounded phosphatic nodules (Itinerary 17A) derived from earlier horizons.

Evaporitic Rocks

Sea-water usually contains about 35 parts per thousand of dissolved salts and waters in the $30-40°/_{oo}$ range are considered normal saline. An increase above $40°/_{oo}$ due to evaporation gives *hypersaline water*, a decrease by addition of fresh water in the range $0.5-20°/_{oo}$ gives *hyposaline* or *brackish water*. When evaporated, sea-water shows a solid residue of elements as follows: chlorine (Cl, 55.2%), sodium (Na, 30.6%), sulphate (SO_4, 7.7%), magnesium (Mg, 3.8%), calcium (Ca, 1.2%), potassium (K, 1.1%), carbonate (CO_3, 0.2%) and bromine (Br, 0.2%). Minerals are precipitated out from sea-water in a regular progression as evaporation takes place but this depends on temperature, atmospheric pressure, amount of circulation and degree of evaporation. A usual order with expected final percentage of salts is: calcite or aragonite ($CaCO_3$) or dolomite ($CaMg(CO_3)_2$, 0.4%), gypsum and anhydrite ($CaSO_4.2H_2O$ and $CaSO_4$, 3.6%), halite or rock salt (NaCl, 78%). Other residual minerals include kieserite ($MgSO_4$, 5.7%), sylvite (KCl, 2.6%) and bischofite ($MgCl_2$, 9.4%), but small amounts of the last two elements also occur in carnallite.

The occurrence of gypsum masses in the Lower Purbeck (Itinerary 22A) or the presence of halite crystal impressions (salt pseudomorphs) at certain levels (Itinerary 17F) suggests evaporation of this type may occur as in non-marine evaporites of present-day *salt lakes* and *salinas*, or in small coastal basins cut off from the sea (as in the Sea of Azov). But more frequently salts may be spread through sediments of coastal plains by seepage or flooding of salt water, as in the *sabkhas* and *salinas* of the Trucial Coast. This leads to crystallisation of minerals within sediments giving very complex mineralogies which may change with time. Such diagenetic histories have been described for the Lower Purbeck Beds by West (1975). The relations of gypsum and anhydrite are particularly complex since above a few hundred metres overburden anhydrite is converted into secondary gypsum by the addition of water.

Progressively shallowing *sabkha cycles* have been described with deeper water and subtidal marls and claystones, followed by oolitic and bioclastic limestones and peloidal limestones. Intertidal facies include *fenestrated limestones* (with small *bird's-eye* cavities) then stromatolitic levels with gypsum pseudomorphs. In supratidal (sabkha) sediments nodular structures with anhydrite occur (*chicken-wire structure*) and anhydrite can occur in irregular *enterolithic* patterns. Several such sequences are known from the Purbeck Beds (Itinerary 17F, 22A, B).

Facies

Clearly different sediments can be formed in different places: these are spoken of as different *facies*, a term introduced by Gressly in 1838 and widely used: *lithofacies* refers to lithological characters, *biofacies* to organic characters and the term is used quite loosely as in *calcareous facies* or *sandstone facies*.

A very wide range of sedimentary facies is represented in the Dorset succession. These enable a facies transect to be illustrated from terrestrial to fairly deep marine. The purpose here is to draw attention to some of the rock types involved and where examples may be seen in the Dorset sequence. More details are given in relation to specific itineraries.

Terrestrial Facies

Climate is a major control of rock facies on land. In dry, *arid* areas, erosion is by flash floods and iron oxides gather near the surface owing to leaching. Deposition occurs as scree slopes and in broad plains or *playas* which may include fine red micrites and evaporites. The Trias exhibits this facies best. If rainfall is high erosion and the washing away of sediment is quick. Such *fluvial* facies are illustrated by the ancient river terraces such as the Lower Palaeolithic Terrace (called in older literature the 100 foot Terrace) around Moreton (Itinerary 16), and there are others in the Bournemouth area. The Tertiary Beds of east Dorset, and the Wealden Beds (Itineraries 17, 18, 23), represent more ancient analogues. When conditions are cold *glacial* or *periglacial* conditions occur as during the Pleistocene. Solifluxion gravels associated with periglacial conditions are widespread in the Weymouth lowlands and are reworked from older chert-dominated gravels.

River deposition illustrating alluvial conditions of playa and transitory lake environments are best represented by the Wealden Beds (Itineraries 17, 18, 23) and Tertiary Beds (Itineraries 25, 26) and these include clastic rocks of a wide range of grain size from lake clays, through plant-bearing sands to quite coarse gravels. Deposits in river systems are extensive and extend out to sea as deltas.

More tranquil lacustrine conditions of carbonate lakes or lagoons are illustrated by the Purbeck Beds (Itineraries 11, 17, 18, 22) but often these show evidence of saline influences from time to time, often cyclically. This shows that the sea was not far away. This, and associated evaporitic levels, thin bedding and widely distributed bedding units suggest low energy environments of hyposaline lagoons with stromatolite, pellet and ostracod limestones and marls. Dominant are calcareous micrites probably originating from algal-derived lime muds. The algae may represent an occasional lake-fringing facies. Such a facies may also be illustrated by the White Lias (Itinerary 1) and the snuff box level of the Inferior Oolite (Itinerary 7) which develops in a shoal-like area southwards from east of Beaminster to the coast around Burton Bradstock.

Marine Carbonate Facies

In shallow waters free from clastic input limestones are often formed. Open marine environments in which were formed varied marine shelly limestones, oolites and mudstones are best illustrated by levels in the Inferior Oolite (Itinerary 7), Corallian Beds (Itinerary 12) and Portland Beds (Itineraries 11, 17, 18, 20) and each has some evidence for shallow water conditions. The nuclei of ooliths of the Osmington Oolite are often quartz grains showing clastic sources were close at hand. Such facies often develop today on extensive offshore shoals as in the Bahamas and Florida Keys.

Deeper-water carbonate facies are best illustrated by the coccolith limestones of the Kimmeridge Clay (Itinerary 19) and especially by the enormously thick planktonic limestones of the Chalk (Itineraries 1, 13, 17). The harder beds in the Chalk and hardgrounds represent shallowing levels when more carbonate cement formed. The term hardground was first used when modern corers could bring up no mud from the sea floor: it is now used for levels which are thought to have cemented early and provided a temporary hard surface on the sea floor.

Marine Arenite Facies

Good deltaic facies are not seen in the Mesozoic of Dorset. The marine sand units, especially the Bridport Sands (Itineraries 6, 7), Nothe Grit and Sandsfoot Grit (Itinerary 12) of the Corallian, probably represent widely spread off-shore sand banks and they have rare examples of storm disturbance, indicating occasional shallow waters. At these levels evidence of burrowing organisms is common. Special sand facies are often associated with sponges, as in the rhaxellid-rich beds of the Portland Sand (Itinerary 11) or the siliceous chert beds of the Upper Greensand (Itinerary 17). Some of the so-called sands of the Portland Beds are now known to be dolomitic siltstones.

The limited ironstones, such as the Abbotsbury Ironstone (Itinerary 8), are rich in quartz grains and probably represent areas protected by an offshore bar where iron concentration was possible.

Marine Argillite Facies

About 70% of the Dorset Jurassic succession is in a clay facies. Many environments are represented. The association of clays with euryhaline (probably reduced-salinity) oysters in the Fuller's Earth (Itineraries 6, 9) and Portland Sand (Itinerary 11) suggest estuarine influences. Deeper-water clays representing oxic environments usually have a rich bottom living (benthonic) fauna and original lamination has usually been removed by the activity of burrowing organism, a process termed *bioturbation*. Anoxic environments are illustrated by paper-shales and kerogen-rich shales where neither bioturbation nor biodegradation on the sea floor was significant. Evidence of anoxia in sediments below the seafloor is often indicated by the formation of authigenic minerals such as the iron sulphides pyrite (common) and marcasite (rare).

5. STRUCTURE

The Mesozoic and Tertiary strata of Dorset have only been gently folded by large-scale earth movements since they were laid down and lithified. Along the Frome Valley from Dorchester east to Poole Harbour (Back Cover, Fig. 1) the Chalk and Tertiary Beds are folded down into a shallow basin forming the *Frome Syncline*, the axis of which passes almost due east from Dorchester to south of Poole. To the south of this, along the hog's-back ridge from Bat's Head (Itinerary 17A, Fig. 32), past Corfe Castle (Itinerary 24C) to Ballard Down (Fig. 38) the Chalk is vertical and forms the middle limb, or *Purbeck Monocline* joining the Frome Syncline with the *Purbeck Anticline* to the south the fold axis of which passes from Kimmeridge to St. Alban's Head. Further west, and south of the Ridgeway is the *Weymouth Anticline*, a broad arch of Jurassic rocks which dip slightly steeper on the north side (Back Cover, Fig. 12) giving an asymmetric anticline. In west Dorset the folds are gentler and the dominant structure is the *Marshwood Dome*, centred 9km northwest of Bridport where the Lower Lias core is almost completely surrounded by younger rocks.

In the Weymouth and Purbeck areas fault and shear structures may be quite intense. It is also clear that two periods of tectonism affected the area. Mid-Cretaceous (pre-Albian) tensional structures had an influence on later Tertiary structures which have compressional features. Locally, substantial downcutting below the Albian, and the nature of the pre-Albian surface and rock fabrics, has led to disharmonic structures.

The Purbeck Monocline is a northward facing monoclinal structure of Tertiary age. In the North Sea such structures are often produced by normal fault reactivation at depth of earlier normal faults by further normal movement so that in younger rocks draped folds can result. By contrast, the Purbeck fold is associated with a mid-Cretaceous (pre-Albian) normal fault with a southerly downthrow at depth, which was reactivated in Tertiary times by reversed movement. As the Purbeck Monocline dies out to the west, other folds and faults are seen, and these show a consistent relation to the pre-Albian structures (Fig. 3).

The Weymouth Anticline is a more complex structure. It is bounded to the north by the Abbotsbury-Ridgeway fault system. The Abbotsbury Fault has a southerly throw and is of pre-Albian date. It passes east into the Ridgeway Fault which has a northerly downthrow and is Tertiary in age. The relation of these structures is illustrated in Figure 22 by an interpretation of the Bincombe railway cutting north of Weymouth. Further east there is a series of synclines, anticlines and periclines south of the Ridgeway Fault (Figs. 21–29) and several of these have been tested for oil traps. Whilst the northern limb of the Weymouth Anticline (to judge from its continuation in the Broadway Anticline) is pre-Albian in age, the geological relations in the English Channel to the south indicate strongly that the southern limb is Tertiary in age and that it corresponds and coalesces with the southern limbs of the Purbeck Monocline and the Isle of Wight Monocline.

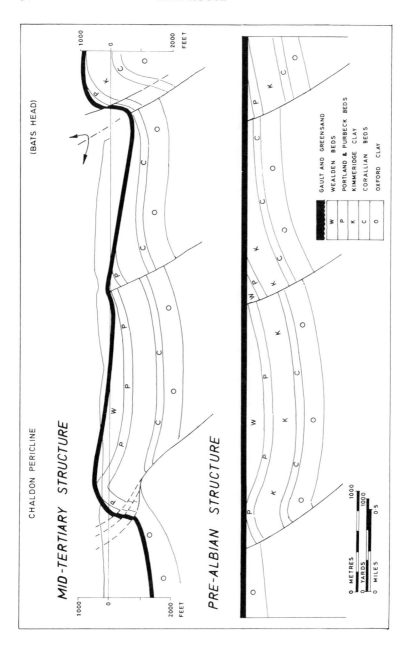

Figure 3.   Tertiary and pre-Albian structures between Chaldon and west of Lulworth
             showing their relationship to pre-Albian faults. Compare with Figure 4.

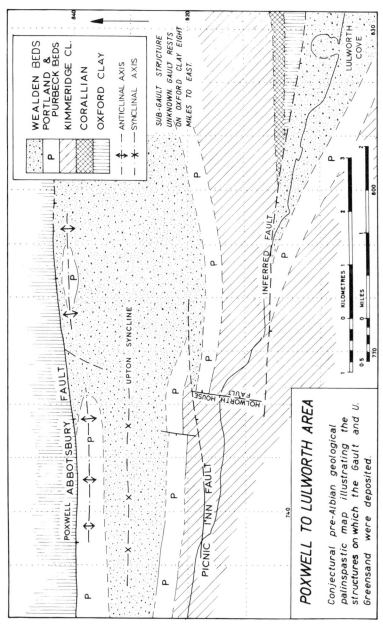

Figure 4.   Palaeogeological map of the Sutton Poyntz–White Nothe area at the time of the deposition of the Gault showing the effects of the pre-Albian movements.

The interplay of pre-Albian and Tertiary structures is particularly well seen at outcrop in the Poxwell to Lulworth area (Fig. 3). Here it is possible to construct the mid-Cretaceous erosion surface on which the Gault and Upper Greensand were deposited and to illustrate the disharmonic relation between the early structures and the later Tertiary ones. Here there is also some subsurface control provided from boreholes at Poxwell, Chaldon and East Lulworth. A resulting interpretation is illustrated in Figure 4.

These relationships showing the effects of earlier faults on later tectonism are very instructive. In the three examples illustrated in Figure 3, there is evidence that the earlier, pre-Albian fault is listric, that is, that the dip of the fault plane shallows to the south with depth. There is borehole evidence for this at Chaldon and Poxwell (Itinerary 15). Noticeable in all three cases is the way in which the Gault transgresses up-dip to the south of the faults. This indicates the existence of a pre-Albian roll-over structure. This is also seen in the Poxwell-Chaldon area (Figs. 26, 27, 29), the South Down Farm area (Fig. 20) and in Durdle Cove (Itinerary 17A). Gibbs (1984) has given a discussion of listric fault geometry showing how this would lead to such erosion on the upthrow side of faults. If this is the correct interpretation of shallow structures it is not clear at what level the horizontal slip is taking place at depth. The thick salt horizons in the Triassic may play a role in this (in the Marshwood borehole there is a Keuper salt unit 71m thick), or the faults may be related to deeper structures in the Hercynian basement (Chadwick 1986). For the three illustrated faults, Tertiary compressional reactivation led to the formation of monoclinal folds, or pop-ups, forming above them (Fig. 3).

These Dorset structures reflect those in southern Britain generally where pre-Albian faults, and especially Triassic to mid-Cretaceous sedimentary basins have led to complex re-activation structures and basin inversion (Chadwick 1993).

In west Dorset the hill and headland summits are capped with Upper Cretaceous beds the base of which, along the coast west of Abbotsbury, is about 90–150m O.D. rising inland to about 245m near Pilsdon Pen. Many of the east-west faults in this western area are probably of mid-Cretaceous date. These may include the Eype Mouth Fault, Bridge and Pucknowle Faults which are responsible for preserving a tract of Cornbrash and younger Jurassic rocks beneath the Cretaceous unconformity inland, northeast and east of Burton Bradstock and southeast of Bridport (Fig. 11). Similarly the Bridport and Symondsbury Faults are two east-west faults just north of Bridport which introduce a rifted strip of Inferior Oolite and Bridport Sands within an outcrop of Middle Lias. Such structures suggest a mid-Cretaceous tensional fault system here as in south Dorset. Additionally here, however, north-east and north-west trending faults are seen inland, such as the Mangerton and Hooke/Wynford Faults, which seem a conjugate system: at least the first of these has a strike-slip element. These are probably Tertiary in age.

6. GEOMORPHOLOGY

The form of the Dorset hills gives evidence of a series of erosion surfaces indicating a progressive drop in sea level from the late Tertiary. Sea level ultimately reached below the present level. During the last ten millenia sea level has risen during the Flandrian transgression and this is illustrated by the drowned valley areas of Christchurch Bay, Poole Harbour and the Backwater and Lodmoor near Weymouth. Guidebooks having been published on the coastal landforms of Dorset (Brunsden and Goudie, 1981, Allison (Ed) 1992), this account need serve only as an introduction to other more general matters.

Drainage

In west Dorset the rivers Lim, Char and Brit drain south into Lyme Bay from a watershed 4–13km to the north. This seems to result from (supposed) Miocene folding of the Marshwood Dome (Wilson et al., 1958) but some of the streams have since captured drainage from north of the fold axis.

More easterly areas are dominated by the River Frome which rises north in the Dorset Heights near Evershot (ST 576047), passes beside Dorchester, and then flows east to Poole Harbour (Fig. 1) where it is thought (in former times of lower sea level) to have joined a 'Solent River' to flow east between the Isle of Wight and the mainland: it will have received on its route the northern tributaries of the Piddle (joining at Poole Harbour), and the Stour and Lower Avon (joining south-east of Bournemouth). Streams from the south from Purbeck include the Steeple and Byle, the later entrenchment of which gave the promontory at Corfe Castle (Plate 31B), and other streams in the area south-east of Dorchester where wind gaps, as at Poxwell, show evidence of capture from the south. All these streams suggest a relationship with the Frome Syncline and the foresyncline of the Purbeck and Isle of Wight Monoclines.

High Level Peneplanes

The high points in central southern England suggest an ancient peneplane, the remnants of which now reach heights of around 300m. Whether this irregular surface is wholly of post-Miocene folding date is now doubted, and it is clear that effects of very early Tertiary erosion are important. The high level surface in west Dorset continues to rise in east Devon in a way consistent with an early Tertiary age (Waters 1960).

It is thought that the present drainage system was developed from a marine erosion surface at about 180–200m height. This would have given a coastline skirting south of Black Down at Hardy's Monument (Itinerary 8C) and passing north, then east across the northern Dorset Heights. The present drainage would have developed as the sea retreated, giving the Frome/Solent drainage pattern of today. A similar topographic bench in Kent, also at about 200m, is associated with sediments known as the Lenham Beds, and the fossils found in them were formerly thought to be of Pliocene age, but are now thought to be late Miocene (Curry et al., 1978). A suggestion that the Lenham Beds are glacially moved is not generally accepted. Thus a marine bevelling at about 200m above present sea level may have closely followed the main period of Miocene folding.

In the light of this hypothesis the summit heights along the Dorset coastal area may be examined. The data are as follows (from east to west with an indication of the solid rocks which occur beneath the superficial deposits):

TERTIARY BEDS FORMING SUMMIT

Creechbarrow	(SY 922824)	191m
Bronkham Hill	(SY 626868)	205
Black Down	(SY 613877)	237

CRETACEOUS BEDS FORMING SUMMIT

Godlingston Hill	(SZ 008813)	200
Ridgeway Hill	(SY 914817)	200
Whiteway Hill	(SY 876809)	185
Wears Hill	(SY 556865)	215
Lewesdon Hill	(ST 435013)	272
Golden Cap	(SY 407922)	191
Lambert's Castle	(SY 371987)	256

JURASSIC ROCKS FORMING SUMMIT

Swyre Head	(SY 934785)	207
Pilsdon Pen	(ST 413014)	276

Thus a level at about 200m produces a bevelling across rocks of several ages and across the fold structures of the area. Higher summits would be part of an earlier history which has not been elucidated.

Arkell (1947) argued that since the Frome drainage system is regarded as having resulted directly from the Miocene folding it is unlikely to have an extreme antiquity. When the sea retreated from a 200m level, however, it is possible that a drainage developed which eroded first the softer Tertiary sediments. It is now realised that the Frome Syncline itself rests on a line of even more ancient New Red Sandstone rifting, and it may be that this development was enhanced by further slight subsidence along the line of the Frome synclinal axis.

Low Level Peneplanes and Terraces

When the Weymouth lowlands are viewed from Hardy's Monument (Itinerary 8C), evidence of a succession of lower level planations is apparent. These were analysed in detail by Sparks (1953) who recognised fragments of higher stage platforms 146, 131, 116, 100 and 88m (OD or above Ordnance Datum at sea level). Lower stage platform levels were recognised at about 73, 58, 45 and 14 metres (OD). Of these it is the 73m (formerly 240 foot terrace) level which is the most widespread and dominates the view of the Weymouth lowland from the Portesham area and forms the long bevelled ridges east of Langton Herring, south of Shilvinghampton and at Fleet Common. Similar platforms were considered to be present in the Hampshire Basin (Everard 1957) and in the Weald. These were taken to represent erosional stages in a falling sea level.

There are gravels associated with many of these levels, but they are usually angular or subangular flint and chert gravels with subsidiary rounded clasts, including rare Budleigh Salterton pebbles, which are likely to have been recycled several times. These do not suggest wave-eroded beach gravels. Probably they originated from alluvial gravels and moved as periglacial and solifluxion sludge gravels from higher levels, such as those on Black Down, and spread over lower levels under Pleistocene Ice Age conditions.

The lower platforms of east Dorset have usually been related to terraces of the Frome/Solent system and were studied by Bury (1933) and Green (1946, 1947) especially. There is a succession of morphological terraces in the Bournemouth area which are parallel with the Frome/Solent watercourse. These become progressively lower towards the south. Green correlated the terrace (36–46m) which caps the Bournemouth to Boscombe Cliffs (Itinerary 26) with the Boyn Hill Terrace of the Thames. The Moreton Terrace (Itinerary 16A) lies at about 30m above the present Frome River and the Christchurch Terrace (6.5–7m) caps the low cliffs between Southbourne and Hengistbury Head (Fig. 41D).

Given an early river system along the Frome Valley to the Solent, there will have come a time when the sea will have breached the hog's back ridge of near vertical chalk between Ballard Down and the Isle of Wight passing through a stage represented by Worbarrow Bay today. This is thought to have taken place during the Flandrian transgression of the last 10,000 years or so, which has also led to the drowning of Poole Harbour and Christchurch Bay.

Buried Channels

The buried channels associated with the 'Solent' River system have been located using seismic techniques by Dyer (1975); they can reach to at least 18m below O.D. There is in addition a buried channel, 26m below OD, between Portland and Small Mouth which may date from about 8800 BP (Carr and Blackley 1974); this confirms that a distinct drainage system south of the Frome valley had developed by that time, which had the Wey and the 'Fleet stream' as tributaries.

Chesil Beach

The Chesil Beach is perhaps the most spectacular storm beach in the country. A course at right angles to the middle of the beach aligns between Lizard and Ushant to give an uninterrupted fetch of ocean for 8000km (5000 miles) from the Caribbean, with direct access for strong winds and waves resulting from the main north Atlantic belt of easterly moving depressions and secondary depressions. The Beach extends from Chesilton, where it abuts the cliffs of the Isle of Portland, and stretches to the north-west in a curve to beyond West Bay and, if the recent and artificial breaching of the beach there by the River Brit is taken to give an arbitrary western limit, the length is about 28km (17.4 miles). For 13km the Beach is separated from the mainland by the tidal lagoon of the Fleet which formerly drained into Portland Harbour at Small Mouth (or Ferry Bridge) but which has recently been artificially diverted. Useful reviews of opinions on the origin and nature of Chesil Beach have been given by Carr and

Blackley (1969, 1973, 1974) and observations relating to a storm in 1978 by Gibbs (1982). The main points of access referred to in the present itineraries are at West Bay (Itinerary 6), Abbotsbury (Itinerary 8), and Portland (Itinerary 11).

Chesil Beach reaches a maximum width of about 200m opposite Fleet village, and narrows towards both extremities. In height it is at a maximum of 14.7 m O.D. at Chesilton. Some 98.5% of the constituent pebbles are of flint and chert with the remainder of Budleigh Salterton-type quartzites, vein quartz, rare porphyries, granites and metamorphic pebbles but with limestones common at the Chesil end.

The systematic and gradual change in size of pebbles on the beach from large cobbles at the Portland end, to grains of small pea size at the western end is well known. It is presumed that large blocks out of grade are moved south-westward by a zig-zag movement of onshore and down-beach movement: this indicates that the average wind fetch is slightly to the north of the line at right angles to the middle of the beach. The importance of the faster lateral movement of any pebbles not in grade has been documented, and tracer material out of grade has been shown to migrate at rates up to 340m in 24hrs. Carr (1969) has shown that shape of pebbles is about constant along the length of the beach. MacFadyen (1970) has noted evidence suggesting that pebble size has reduced slightly in historic time.

The steep seaward and usually concave face of the beach records, as bench levels or 'wracks', the notches produced in the beach profile by the specific storms and tides in the past, the oldest being at the top. The gently-sloping landward face steepens against the Fleet and this is often emphasised and probably caused by seepages which can give shingle spreads and hollows or 'cans'. Pebbles are thrown over to the landward side in exceptional storms. Recent storms have added an observable spread of such unstained light-coloured pebbles at the Chesilton end, where a recent sea-wall has been erected with drainage to try to stop water flooding Chesilton during storms. Floods are at their worst when there is a conjunction of high spring tides, low barometric pressures and gales.

Bedrock is exposed in many places on the sea floor of West (or Lyme) Bay (Donovan and Stride 1961, Penn et al. 1980). Boreholes along Chesil Beach (Carr and Blackley 1973) show that the foundation for the shingle is a planed-off bedrock surface rising landward to meet the steeper slope of the inland hills with a break of slope associated with a more ancient storm beach which is at a depth of −15m opposite East Fleet. Peat underlying the beach, at about −2 and −5m O.D. has given radiometric dates of around 4900−5400 years BP (before the present day) but there is an age of 6100 BP from opposite Wyke Regis. It is supposed that Chesil Beach has migrated from the southwest by wave and roll-over movement to come to lie on these ancient peats. It is assumed, therefore, that the low hills of Weyland were not affected by the Flandrian transgression but date from earlier interglacial erosion and this view is supported by the presence of plateau gravels on topographic flats in that area (Sparks 1951, House 1961).

Portland Raised Beach

The nature of the Portland raised beaches has usually been discussed in relation to Chesil Beach despite the fact that the fetch is in a different direction. Recent work has shown that there are two separate raised beaches at the southern end of Portland (Itinerary 11F) and that they are of very much greater antiquity (125,000 and 210,000 years BP, Davies and Keen 1985) (Itinerary 11F).

7. ECONOMIC GEOLOGY

The geological resources of the area have been used since time immemorial in the service of man. The use of flint and chert for axe, spear and arrow heads is known from Palaeolithic times. Large sarsens were gathered from the basal Tertiary to construct ceremonial rings on the Dorset downs. Large stone blocks of other material were gathered for tombs and there are examples of many stone types, including Kimmeridge Oil Shale, in Bronze Age burials (Itinerary 8E). The Romans exploited stone in a more systematic way for their settlements and for towns such as Dorchester.

Until the age of mechanisation and cheap transport local materials were almost invariably used and this is reflected in the nature of the older buildings. Thus building materials reflect local sources. In the limestone areas of Portland and Purbeck great use was and is made of Portland and Purbeck Stone. In the Tertiary areas in the Frome valley the clays and loams of the Reading Beds and other horizons were used for brick making as at Broadmayne. This was developed even more in areas of the Oxford Clay around Weymouth and east of Bridport and in areas of Lias clays of eastern Dorset. Brickmaking in Dorset is discussed in an excellent review by Young (1972) but it is now almost defunct.

The thin limestones of the Lower Lias were extracted for cement, curb stones and wall materials. Until well into this century most farms which had clay soils needed lime and this was provided from many local limekilns along the outcrops of the Inferior Oolite, Cornbrash, Corallian and Portland Beds especially. Traces of many of these kilns still remain. The Lower Chalk was worked locally for the manufacture of cement and there are many old quarries at this level at the foot of the chalk downs. Wherever good stone was freely available this was preferred for wall-making and local buildings.

Rather more specialist rock products are the excellent pipe and ball clays of the early Tertiary worked near Corfe Castle (Itinerary 24B, C) and near Poole where it formed the centre of the Poole pottery industry. Even in the 18th century this area was supplying clay to the Staffordshire potteries. The Abbotsbury Iron Ore (Itinerary 8A) was surveyed for large-scale iron production in the First World War (1914–1918), fortunately, for the village, without success. Other levels of ironstones in Tertiary sands will doubtless have been used for local iron production in Mediaeval and earlier times.

Modern requirements for cheap building materials have led to the use of gravels and sands as aggregates in concretes and cements. As a result there are now extensive quarries in the Tertiary Beds of the Frome valley (Itinerary 16A).

The use of pebbles from the Chesil Beach for more special purposes is now severely restricted. For higher-quality freestone work both Portland Stone (Itinerary 11) and Purbeck Stone (Itinerary 21B) is in demand, but mostly for export from the region. There has been a use of limestones from these levels for reconstituted stone cast in moulds for particular shapes. For over three centuries London and other cities were easily reached by cheap sea-transport and have used Dorset stone.

Water supply reflects the geology and the chalk downs provided the major source in the past and still do so today. Spring lines follow the junction of the Chalk and Upper Greensand with the impermeable Gault Clay below and ancient hamlets and villages are sited along these lines. In other areas wells have to be sunk to the water-table and much deeper to ensure a supply in times of drought.

The development of oil resources is new apart from the abortive attempts to extract oil from the Blackstone or Kimmeridge Oil Shale by distillation in the last century; the Blackstone producing up to 120 gallons of oil and 9,000 cubic feet of gas to the ton (Strahan 1898, p. 54). Before the Second World War (1939–1945) the D'Arcy Exploration Company investigated suitable structures and drilled boreholes in south Dorset but none were productive. This was continued after the War by the British Petroleum Company who in 1959 started producing oil from the Kimmeridge well (Itinerary 19A). More spectacular were the discoveries by the British Gas Corporation which led in 1973 to production from Wytch Farm field (Itinerary 25C) which is already the largest onshore well in the country and with the development of the adjacent areas and deeper levels will become the largest onshore field in Europe.

ITINERARIES

I WEST DORSET COAST

This stretch of the Dorset coast exposes Jurassic rocks dipping gently to the south. The Jurassic is capped, on higher cliffs, by unconformable middle Cretaceous (Albian). Only minor faults and folds interrupt the continuous exposures along the coast. The classic sections of the Lower Jurassic near Lyme Regis were made famous in the early years of the last century by the discovery of ichthyosaurs, plesiosaurs, and pterosaurs by Mary Anning (1800–1847; Lang 1938, 1956) and the Misses Philpot (Edmonds 1978).

The Lias succession is summarised in Figure 6. The Lower Lias was described by W.D. Lang (1924, 1936, Lang et al., 1923, 1926, 1928, reviewed by Hallam 1989), and faunal lists have been usefully updated by Palmer (1972) and Page (1992). The Middle Lias has been described by M.K. Howarth (1957) and the Upper Lias by J.F. Jackson (1922, 1926). The Bridport and Yeovil Memoir (Wilson et al., 1958) provides a convenient summary. Recent selected sediment-ological and palaeontological work has been published by Hallam (1960, 1967, 1975), Sellwood (in Sellwood et al., 1970) and Jenkyns and Senior (1977) but more exhaustive systematic and interpretative work is long overdue.

Road access to the coast is made at the river and stream outlets at Lyme Regis, Charmouth, Seatown, Eype Mouth, West Bay and Burton Bradstock. The notes given here are based on those access points with convenient car parks. Traverses along the shore are necessary to examine the whole section, but these should only be attempted at favourable tides. The shore below some of the cliffs can be extremely dangerous at high tide when there may be no escape. The cliff base can be hazardous at all times, but especially after rains, through stones falling at high velocity. The Dorset Coastal Path gives a right of way along the cliff top but, apart from the road access points under which the itineraries are listed, there are few routes up to the top. Landslips and falls alter the section visible from time to time. The area of Ware Cliffs (Fig. 7) is a National Nature Reserve and those intending to study geology away from the public coastal footpath should contact the Nature Conservancy's South-West Regional Office at Roughmoor, Bishops Hall, Taunton, TA1 5AB (Tel. (0823) 83211) for a permit and up-to-date safety information. Advice is also available at the Charmouth Heritage Coast Centre, Lower Sea Lane, Charmouth.

A separate guide deals with the coastal landforms of West Dorset (Allison 1992) and especially the coastal landslips so these aspects are only cursorily mentioned in this guide.

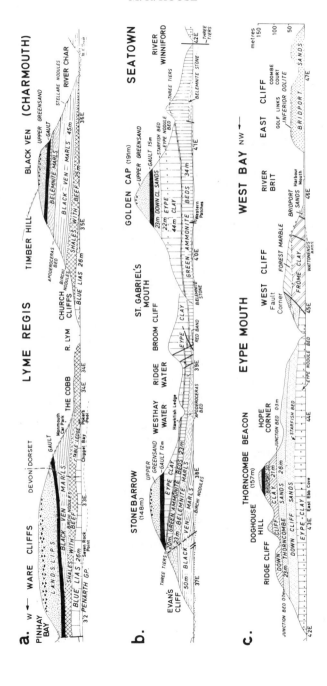

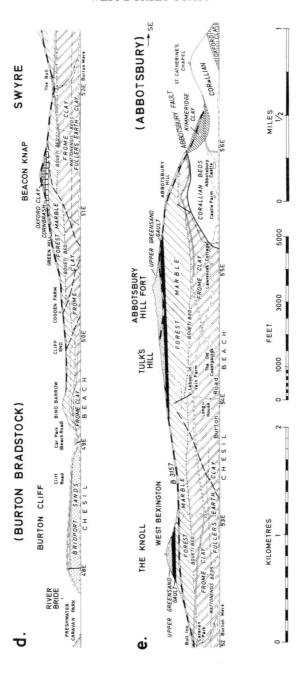

Figure 5. Coastal sections of the West Dorset coast from Pinhay Bay to Abbotsbury.
Vertical exaggeration ×3.

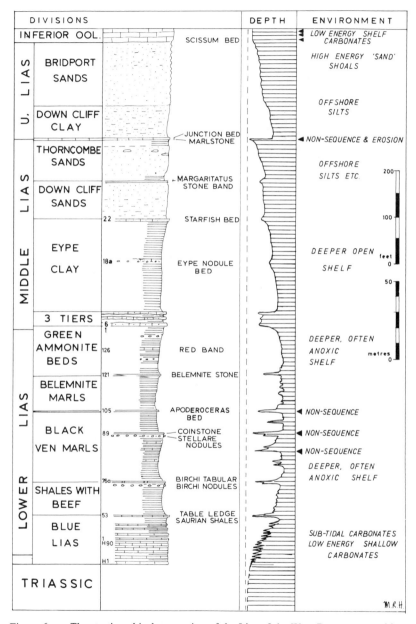

Figure 6.   The stratigraphical succession of the Lias of the West Dorset coast with an indication of possible depositional environments.

1. PINHAY BAY

There is a long-stay car park off the A3052 (SY 336920) at the top of the hill west of Lyme Regis before the turn down to The Cobb. A footpath, often rough and messy, leads west from the long-stay car park direct to Pinhay Warren through the undercliff jungle of Ware Cliffs (Fig. 7) where a descent can sometimes be made to the shore at Pinhay Bay west of the fault (at SY 318908) but mud flows and rock falls recently have made this treacherous. More usually it is necessary to continue 400m west by the private road, soon encountered, to the Pumping Station below Chapel Rock (just off the map on Fig. 7) and here an easier descent (or ascent) is always possible about 80m west of a small waterfall (over Best Bed, Bed 41 in Fig. 9). This locality can also be reached if tides permit by following the shore route from The Cobb (Itinerary 2B) and this is more rewarding but this reverses the stratigraphical and geographical order followed here.

1A. Chapel Rock (SY 315906). This locality (just off the margin of Fig. 8) is passed near the pumping station on the route down to the shore at Pinhay Bay. The Cretaceous succession here is as follows:

CLAY WITH FLINTS	1m
UPPER CHALK	26
MIDDLE CHALK	44
LOWER CHALK (Beer Head Limestone)	1
UPPER GREENSAND	
CHERT BEDS	25
FOXMOULD	43
GAULT	8
(LOWER LIAS BELOW)	

The region between Axmouth and Lyme Regis is famous for its landslips (Arber 1973, Pitts 1982, 1984, Grainger *et al.*, 1986). They are also important west and east of Charmouth (Allison (Ed) 1992). The region around Chapel Rock illustrates the typical landslip structure. Here water held in the glauconitic sands of Foxmould and Chert Beds (Upper Greensand) below the Chalk continually lubricates the plastic clays of the Gault and Lias and foundering results (Grainger *et al.*, 1986). There is a good section through the Chalk here (Fig. 8) which was described by Rowe (1903) and Jarvis and Tocher (1987, p. 58).

1B. Head of Pinhay Bay (SY 318908). Here Triassic rocks of the Penarth Group are exposed. On the foreshore just east of the fault (Fig. 7) the Contorta Shales (5m) of the Westbury Formation (Rhaetic) crop out with the bivalves *Rhaetavicula contorta*, *Chlamys valoniensis* and *Protocardia rhaetica*. In the overlying Lilstock Formation, the Cotham Member (1.5m) has a thin algal level at the top (which is the equivalent of the Cotham (Landscape) Marble of the Bristol area). This is followed by the White Lias of Langport Member (7.8m) seen in the cliff which comprises pale cream or grey micritic pure limestones. The present cliff (Plate 1A) shows a 1.74m unit (Bed A) at the base followed by up to 1.4m (Bed B) of light coloured micrite with derived micrite clasts, 2–3m across, at the base and a 10cm limestone above. The overlying 2.6m (Bed C)

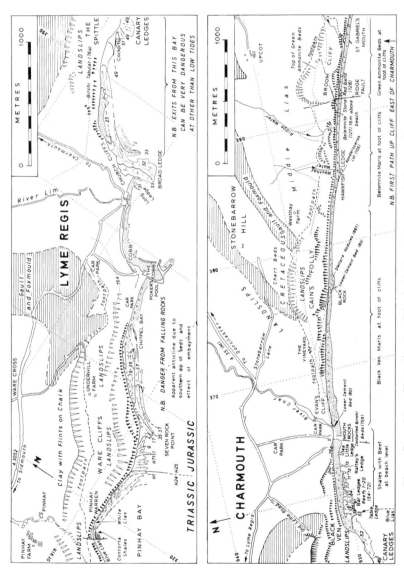

Figure 7.   Maps illustrating localities in the Lyme Regis and Charmouth areas.

N   S

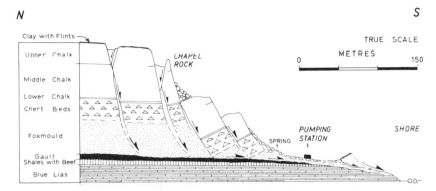

Figure 8.   Geological relations of the landslips near Chapel Rocks just west of Pinhay
             Bay. After Grainger *et al.*, 1986.

shows slumped and algal structures with the Sun Bed, 5cm thick, at the top.
There are intraformational conglomerates, suncracks, erosional and slump
structures and algal-mat laminations with doming. Benthonic marine bivalves
include *Liostrea hisingeri* and corals occur also. The Sun Bed at the top has the
U-shaped burrows of the trace fossil *Diplocraterion*. A shallow marine lagoonal
environment is inferred. The White Lias is seen on the foreshore at low tides east
towards Seven Rock Point.

1C. West of Seven Rock Point (SY 323907). Higher and younger rocks are
seen by walking along the beach to the east (Plate 1A). The overlying Blue Lias
(19m), described in detail by Lang (1924), consists of alternating units of shale
(up to 1.8m) and limestone (up to 0.3m). Only the lowest 2.5m (Beds H1−24
of Lang 1924, sometimes called the pre-*planorbis* Beds and excluded from the
Blue Lias) is included in the uppermost Trias Penarth Group and Lilstock
Formation. This is because in Bed H25 (Fig. 9) the near-smooth subevolute
ammonite *Psiloceras* enters, defining the base of the Jurassic and of the
Hettangian Stage. Thus the new, supposedly lithostratigraphic terminology
(Warrington *et al.*, 1980), merely apes the chronostratigraphy. Bed 25 is readily
accessible low in the cliff about 540m east of the Pinhay Bay Fault between two
rills (Plate 1B). A 0.25m unit (Bed H30) of compact limestone, 2.35m above the
beach, overlies 0.73m of shale (H29) with two limestone units below (H26−28),
10cm and 18cm thick. The underlying shale (Bed 25, 15cm thick) yields
Psiloceras and marks the base of the Jurassic. Bed 25 drops to sea level on the
east side of Seven Rock Point. The facies succession upward from the White Lias
thus indicates progressive deepening of the sea.

2. LYME REGIS

The most convenient starting point is the Monmouth Car Park (SY 337916), west
of The Cobb, and approached from the A3052 west of the centre of Lyme Regis.
Chippel Bay and Seven Rock Point lie to the west. Monmouth Beach was the site

of the landing by the Duke of Monmouth in 1685 as claimant to the throne on the death of Charles II. This Monmouth Rebellion ended with the Duke's death at Sedgemoor, 6 July 1685.

2A. Chippel Bay to Seven Rock Point (SY 333904). The main accessible section of the Blue Lias is in the cliffs between Chippel Bay and Pinhay Bay (Figs. 6, 9). The sections were described in detail by Lang (1924) who used the numbers H1−H9 (total 10.94m) for beds only seen west of Seven Rock Point, and Beds 1−53 (Brick Ledge to Table Ledge, 19m) for the overlying sequence which commences in the centre of Chippel Bay, and in the core of an apparent anticline (not a true fold but due to the cliff embayment and a regular southward dip of the strata).

The main impure limestones were given distinctive names by quarrymen (Fig. 9) when the beds were worked along the foreshore for cement and building stone. These are most easily recognisable upwards from the core of the 'anticline' in Chippel Bay. The Brick Ledge (Bed 1, 0.76m) comprises six thin limestones with undulating surfaces separated by thin shales which are the lowest beds seen (when not obscured by the beach gravels). Specketty (Bed 19, 0.71m higher and *ca.* 0.3m thick) is here about 1.5m above beach level (Plate 3). About 50m west of a small fault Mongrel (Bed 23, 0.2m) forms a ledge at the beach top, which holds pools of water in hollows on an irregular upper surface. The limestone contains nests of brachiopods *Calcirhynchia calcarea* and occasional *Gryphaea arcuata* Group and the dip takes it down the beach in the next 70m and then the outcrop curves back towards The Cobb and exposes below it the kerogen-rich shales of Bed 22. The Second Tape (Bed 27, 0.23m thick) is 0.3m above and the upper surface has very large ammonites up to 0.5m in diameter. To the west, and 0.24m higher, is a wide ledge with scattered *Gryphaea* and ammonites about 13cm diameter, which is Top Tape (Bed 29, 0.25m thick). Third Quick (Bed 31, 0.3m) is 0.48m higher and forms a long beach parallel with the cliff. Grey Ledge (Bed 49) is a distinctive marker.

Ammonites are used to subdivide the succession. Schlotheimid ammonites (strongly-ribbed derivatives of *Psiloceras*) characterise the Blue Lias up to Bed 20 (0.2m above Specketty (Bed 19)). Thereafter the entry of arietitid ammonites (with keels on the venter, ribbed flanks and often giant size), such as *Coroniceras*, mark the base of the Sinemurian Stage. The black-shelled bivalve *Plagiostoma gigantea* is common at several levels and specimens get progressively larger through the succession.

The origin of the small sedimentary microrhythms in this part of the sequence has been much debated. Typically the rhythms start with a thin, kerogen-rich black shale, without benthos and perhaps 'varved' (Plate 4A), followed by grey shales with some fossils and evidence of loss of primary lamination, which pass up generally by a sharp but irregularly-burrowed contact into the base of the overlying grey impure limestone, the burrows (Plate 2B) being mainly coarsely branching *Thalassinoides* (crustacean burrows), *Chondrites* (originally a downward branching spaghetti-like feeding burrow) and the obliquely U-shaped dwelling burrows of *Rhizocorallium* (perhaps produced by polychaete worms). Colonisation sequences can be elucidated. The limestone cementation is thought to be early diagenetic. Indeed, it has been argued that the burrowing enhanced

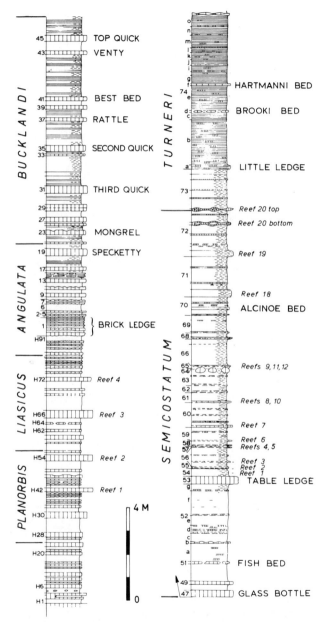

Figure 9.   The Blue Lias and early Shales with Beef. Largely based on data of W.D.
Lang. The top of the Blue Lias is drawn at Table Ledge (after House 1985b).

the carbonate cementation (House 1987). It is thought that the alternation of limestones and shales reflects sea level or climate changes induced by changes in insolation received from the Sun and are orbitally forced (House 1985). The typical cycle may have lasted about 40,000 years and may correspond to the cycle of the Obliquity of the Ecliptic. Weedon (1986) has statistically demonstrated that other cycles are represented and suggests that there are gaps in the sequence.

The top of the Blue Lias is taken at Table Ledge (Bed 53, 0.3m) The 3m below this are referred to as the Saurian Shales, and these have provided most of the known reptiles, especially where they once formed broad ledges, as near Canary Ledges (Fig. 7). The overlying Shales with Beef (Beds 54–76, 25m) include only very thin limestones or concretions and differ markedly from the Blue Lias below and a deeper-water environment of formation is inferred for them. The prominent line of concretions seen high above the Monmouth car park is the Birchi Nodular (Bed 75a), named after the ammonite *Microderoceras birchi*, and 0.3m higher is the Birchi Tabular (Bed 76a), which marks the base of the Black Ven Marls.

The shore between The Cobb and Pinhay Bay is littered not only with Liassic material, but with blocks of Cretaceous from the high cliffs inland. Calcarenites of the Albian Upper Greensand with calcareous serpulid worm tubes, diverse trace fossils and intraformational conglomerates occur and there are spectacular mauve and purple translucent cherts derived from the Chert Beds.

2B.   Lyme (SY 342921). Car parks in central Lyme Regis enable visits to be made to the Museum and to the local fossil shops. From here there is easy access to Church cliffs and the foreshore east towards Black Ven. This area is not recommended except at very low tides since the exits are dangerous with a rising tide.

3.   CHARMOUTH

Rapid coastal erosion is leading to landslips and cliff recession especially west of Charmouth. Hammering is a sensitive local issue and should be restricted. Attention is drawn to the fact that when working eastward along the coast there is no way up the cliff until St Gabriel's Mouth is reach where access can be made to the cliff top path for the long return walk to Charmouth. Barney's Fossil Shop is 100m east of the George Hotel on the main road, but Mr Barney has now died and the future of the shop is uncertain.

3A.   Old Lyme Road (SY 359936). Vivid evidence of coastal landslips is seen if the Old Lyme Road (locally called the Roman Road) is followed off the A35(T) west of Charmouth from where access is gained (at SY 357933) to the top of the landslips. See map in Allison (1992, p. 65). Here foundered villas bear witness to the victory of erosion over the optimism of man. At the head of the now terminating road, good sections of the Cretaceous are well seen with a basal Gault (12m) of loamy glauconitic sand with a basal conglomerate, Cowstones (6m) of sandstone concretions, the Foxmould (21m) of grey and yellow-weathering glauconitic sands through which the old road passed, with overlying Chert Beds with the fossil oyster *Exogyra obliquata* [=*E.conicum*] and the ammonite *Mortoniceras*; the Foxmould has *Mortoniceras* and *Hysteroceras* and all are indicative of the late Albian. If a descent is made into the amphitheatre, parts of Green Ammonite Beds, Belemnite Marls and upper Black Ven Marls can be seen (Figs. 6, 7) with varying degrees of difficulty and inadvisability. The higher Lower Lias levels are better seen west of Seatown.

3B. Charmouth Beach (SY 366929). Near the George Hotel in Charmouth, Lower Sea Lane leads to the shore. Immediately west of the car park at the beach the Birchi Nodules (Bed 75a) are seen in the low cliffs. They are folded by valley bulging and a local fault where the stream runs out to the sea and this may be exposed when the shingle is down. At low water traces of a submerged forest, with remains of ash and birch tree trunks and bones of mammoth and red deer have been found close to the western groyne (Lang 1961, J.B. Land *in* Cope 1976). The Charmouth Heritage Coast Centre, above a cafe, has a small museum.

The Shales with Beef (22m) are seen to the west below the Birchi Nodules and have common ammonites including *Arnioceras*, *Coroniceras* and *Cymbites*, teeth and bones of ichthyosaurs, many other reptiles (Delair 1958−1960), and a reduced benthonic fauna. These are best seen, when landslips allow, especially in the foreshore reefs which Lang (in Lang *et al.*, 1923) measured in detail. His bed numbers are shown approximately on an accompanying map (Fig. 7: based on a more detailed map published by Lang). Table Ledge (Bed 53), which forms the top of the Blue Lias, crops out below Black Ven and the lowest 12m of the overlying Shales with Beef are blue-grey conchoidal marls with the ammonites *Arnioceras* and *Euagassiceras*, capped by Little Ledge (Bed 74a), a 20cm limestone with 'beef' (fibrous calcite) and marly bands. The overlying beds up to the Birchi Nodules include fissile kerogen-rich shales, and 'beef' is rarer than below. *Arnioceras*, *Caenisites* and *Cymbites* are common ammonites and fine specimens of *Microderoceras birchi* occur near the top and in the Birchi Nodule Bed. The higher Black Ven Marls can be examined best below Stonebarrow.

3C. Stonebarrow (SY 377928). A detailed account of the classic landslips in the cliffs of Stonebarrow has been published by Brunsden and Jones (1976). Erosion of the soft Black Ven Marls in the lower part of the cliffs leads to foundering of the overlying Belemnite Marls and higher Lias beds and of the Cretaceous beds which cap the hill. Above the Belemnite Marl landslips occur mainly by rotational slides the units of which dip landward. The Black Ven Marls (43m), above the Birchi Tabular may usually be examined east from Charmouth Beach between Evan's Cliff and Stonebarrow (Lang *et al.*, 1926) (Fig. 7). At 11m and 15m above the base are calcareous concretions of the Lower Cement Bed (Bed 80) and Upper Cement Bed, or Pavior (Bed 82). At 17.6m above the base is the Stonebarrow Flatstone (Bed 83), celebrated for its fine specimens of *Asteroceras turneri*, often preserved in yellow and brown calcite, and its insect fauna (Whalley 1985) of beetles, grasshoppers, water-bugs, dragonflies and occasional plant remains of conifers. The succeeding shales are richly fossiliferous with ammonites, nests of rhynchonellids (Ager 1956−1967), insects and fish remains, and The Pentacrinite Bed (0.5m, Bed 84b) has the magnificently preserved crinoid *Pentacrinites fossilis* (Sims 1986).

At 10m above the Flatstone is a prominent line of nodules called the Stellare Nodules (Bed 88f) after the common ammonite *Asteroceras stellare*: these form The Mumbles Reef, 1250m east of the outlet of the River Char (Fig. 7), 2.1m below which is the Limestone with Brachiopods (Bed 87) containing rhynchonellids and bivalves. This is evidence for shallowing water conditions and this is further indicated by the Coinstone (Bed 89), 0.8m above the Stellare Nodules, and marking the top of the Obtusum Zone, the cake-like concretions of which have been pyritised, encrusted and bored and indicate a contemporary hardground. Immediately above is a faunal non-sequence and three or four ammonite subzones of the Obtusum and Oxynotum zones are missing on the coast which are present further north. The succeeding dark shales and marls are highly pyritic and carry a well-preserved ammonite fauna including *Echioceras* (keeled with strong lateral ribs), *Oxynoticeras* (discus-shaped), *Eoderoceras* (with paired lateral spines), and many others may be found among masses of pyrite concentrated by wave action on the beach below Stonebarrow. A sudden increase in water depth is indicated. The Hummocky (Bed 103), 13.7m above the Coinstone is taken as the top of the Black Ven Marls: 4m below the top is the Watch Ammonite Stone (Bed 99), full of *Echioceras*. The Hummocky is full of *Echioceras* and there is a non-sequence marking the junction between the Sinemurian and Pliensbachian stages.

The Belemnite Marls (23m) are bluish-grey marls contrasting in their paler colour and greater carbonate content with the beds below. They form a more massive, vertical cliff than the beds below. At the base is the Apoderoceras or Armatus Limestone (Bed 105), a 0.35m limestone which crops out as a reef at Westhay Water (Fig. 5b). The Marls above are famous for belemnites, which were monographed by Lang (in Lang *et al.*, 1928) but ammonites are common and include the pyritised, compressed and keeled *Tropidoceras* and also *Apoderoceras*, *Platypleuroceras* and *Beaniceras*. The top of the unit is taken at the Belemnite Stone (Bed 121, 0.15m) a laterally persistent limestone full of belemnites, ammonites, bivalves and with some rhynchonellids. It also crops out on either side of Golden Cap (Fig. 5b). Higher units of the Lias are seen further east, but a return should now be made to Charmouth Beach unless a long excusion is intended.

3D. Broom Cliff and St Gabriel's Mouth (SY 396923). There is a zig-zag path down the cliff at St Gabriel's Mouth (SY 390925) 4km east of the mouth of the Char at Charmouth. From Broom Cliff to Golden Cap the Green Ammonite Beds form the lower cliffs (Fig. 5b). East of Stonebarrow Cliff they are 16m thick, but they increase eastward. The Red Band (Bed 126, 1.7m) of the reddish-weathering concretions and marls forms a good marker in the middle of the unit. Below the Red Band the ammonites *Aegoceras*, *Androgynoceras*, and the *Liparoceras* are common: above *Oistoceras* and *Liparoceras* are common (the ammonite fauna was monographed by Spath (in Lang *et al.*, 1983) and discussed by Callomon (1963) in a classic paper on sexual dimorphism in ammonites). Brachiopods also are common (Muir Wood 1936a). In the top three metres *Amaltheus stokesi* (falcate-ribbed and compressed) enters and marks the base of the Upper Pliensbachian (Domerian) stage. This may be a convenient point from which to climb Golden Cap.

4. SEATOWN

This area is reached by following the narrow shore road just opposite Castle Inn in Chideock. There is a small car park at Seatown (SY 420917) recommended here. For Golden Cap hill itself there is a National Trust car park (SY 412934) just off the A35(T) 1.6km west of Chideock.

4A. Golden Cap (SY 406922). Westward from the car park at Seatown is seen the profile of Golden Cap (Fig. 5b). The lowest cliff is formed of the Green Ammonite Beds (now 34m thick) and the hard siltstone courses of the Three Tiers (10m) form the first bench. The Eype Clay (66m) above is followed by some 23m of Down Cliff Sands and the unconformable Cretaceous forms the uppermost 60m of the hill. From some 3m below the Three Tiers upwards the Jurassic sequence is wholly Middle Lias: the bed numbers now used are those of Howarth (1957). The various units are opportunistically available for examination by judicious climbing.

The Belemnite Stone (Bed 121, 0.2m), at the top of the Belemnite Marls, rises westward in the cliff 300m west of the Seatown outlet but, as a result of small faults and folds, it remains close to sea level all around Golden Cap and forms Western Patches Reef, where it is well exposed. It contains many belemnites especially *Passaloteuthis* and *Hastites*, and the ammonites *Beaniceras, Liparoceras, Lytoceras* and *Tragophylloceras*. These and accompanying benthonic molluscs and brachiopods were illustrated by Lang *et al.* (1936).

Fallen blocks of the three bands of micaceous silty sandstone which comprise the Three Tiers (Beds 6–10, 10m) litter the shore below Golden Cap. The Lower Tier (Bed 6) has the ammonite *Amaltheus stokesi* (common) with *Tragophylloceras* and rare *Lytoceras* and there are spectacular trace fossils.

4B. Ridge Cliff (SY 424915). The higher Lias beds are best seen east from Seatown. A very low tide is needed to work this stretch of coast unless the cliff-top path is followed which gives access, often dangerously, to the upper cliff.

The Eype Clay (Beds 9–19, up to 66m) is a series of micaceous blue and grey marls. About 40m above the base is the Eype Nodule Bed (Bed 18a, 0.5m) with irregularly scattered nodules containing the ammonite *Amaltheus stokesi*. This crops out low in the cliffs east of Seatown. Immediately above it is a sandstone unit with the brachiopod *Furcirhynchia furcata*. Day's Shell Bed (Bed 20) is 15m above the Eype Nodule Bed east of Thorncombe Beacon and 20m above it east of Golden Cap. In the Shell Bed Palmer (1966) has recognised about 60 species. The fauna includes many bivalves, including *Entolium, Chlamys, Plagiostoma, Astarte, Liostrea, Modiolus* and others; belemnites include *Passaloteuthis* and *Pseudohastites* and there are also gastropods, echinoderms, ostracods and foraminiferans as well as the ammonite *Amaltheus stokesi*. Palmer interprets the Shell Bed as a winnowed shell accumulate. One metre above it is the Starfish Bed (Bed 22, 1.0m) with the brittle star *Palaeocoma egertoni* and crinoids on the lower surface and within the bed (Goldring and Stephenson 1972, Ensom 1984a).

The sequence continues to show evidence of shallowing water with the Down Cliff Sands (Bed 23, 23–26m) of silts and sands with the occasional brachiopod

Gibbirhynchia muirwoodae and the bivalves *Gryphaea cymbium* and *Pseudo-pecten equivalvis*. Some levels are kerogen-rich. This and higher levels are more readily seen in the gullies cutting the various summits of Thorncombe Beacon. The top of the Sands is taken above the Margaritatus Stone (Bed 24, 0.3m) a reddish-brown weathering band of ironshot grey limestone with the ammonite zone fossil *Amaltheus margaritatus* and also *Am. subnodosus*.

Another sedimentary rhythm is initiated with the Margaritatus Clay (Bed 25, 2m). The overlying Thorncombe Sands (Beds 26–31, 23–26m) comprises sands with calcareous horizons and doggers often locally rich in amaltheids, rhynchonellids, bivalves and *Thalassinoides* burrows and sedimentary structures indicating turbulence. Bioturbation within depositional rhythms increases upwards (Sellwood *et al.*, 1970, p. 726). The overlying Thorncombiensis Bed (Bed 32, 35cm) has the brachiopod *Gibbirhynchia thorncombiensis* and these recur in the overlying clay (Bed 33, 2m): this indicates that the succession is shallowing upwards.

The beds which have been described above the Eype Nodule Bed can be equally well examined westward from Eype Mouth, and levels of the Margaritatus Stone and above are probably better seen east and west of Eype Mouth.

5. EYPE MOUTH

The narrow road to Eype Mouth from the A35, 1.8km west of Bridport and 0.7km east of London Inn, leads south through Eype village to limited parking (SY 447910) near the shore unless parking in a field is possible. At the mouth of the Eype, the Eype Nodule Bed (Bed 18) is raised above sea level by valley bulging. Much of the succession has already been described under the previous Itinerary and the geology here is illustrated on Figure 5c.

5A. Thorncombe Beacon (SY 437914). The Eype Nodule Bed crops out in the cliffs to the west below Thorncombe Beacon (Fig. 5c). Fauna includes the ammonites *Tragophylloceras* (interestingly damaged, Ensom 1985b), *Amaltheus*, *Leptaleoceras*, *Metacymbites* and *Liparoceras* and the rare brachiopod *Davidsonella moorei*. On the east side of Thorncombe Beacon the impersistent Junction Bed is accessible from the cliff top in gullies. This bed comprises a lower unit, Middle Lias in age, known as Marlstone Rock Bed (0.15–0.6m) (Plate 4C) which contains coarsely ribbed amaltheid ammonites of the genus *Pleuroceras* and the brachiopod *Quadratirhynchia* and an upper unit, called the Junction Bed. Several distinct faunas are recognisable despite the thinness of the unit. This completes the rhythm initiated with the Margaritatus Clay. Overlying the Marlstone Rock Bed, and cemented to it, is the Junction Bed, an Upper Lias limestone unit (0.6–1.5m), a condensed deposit also indicating shallowing with several non-sequences and planed surfaces, and ammonites representative of several horizons on the Lower and lower Upper Toarcian (Howarth 1980).

The Down Cliff Clay (21m) represents a late Toarcian deepening phase and late shallowing is indicated by the Bridport Sands, more readily examined farther east. The Cretaceous rocks on Thorncombe Beacon are similar to those at Charmouth (Itinerary 3A) but without the Cowstones lithology.

5B. Fault Corner (SY 450909). East from Eype Mouth a similar sequence can be traced by following the cliff-top path to Fault Corner where the Eype Mouth Fault cuts at a very low angle across the cliff and introduces Middle Jurassic rocks to the east and downthrown side. The fault has a throw of about 200m south and is probably of pre-Albian age. Much of the fault surface is exposed over a distance of some 300m and along it are Junction Bed blocks of differing thickness (0.3–4.0m) and separated by faults. At Fault Corner the Thorncombiensis Bed and overlying clay are missing (Howarth 1957) and the Margaritatus Stone is here 22m below the Junction Bed. Evidence within the Junction Bed of sea-floor fissures or neptunean dykes with late Toarcian faunas (Thouarsense Zone and also of Bifrons anf Falcifer Zone age), is interpreted by Jenkyns and Senior (1977, 1991) to indicate contemporaneous fault activity, but this could have been over a prolonged period. The present-day association with the Eype Mouth Fault may be fortuitous and these tensional effects regional rather than local, or the fault may have been initiated in middle to late Toarcian times and reactivated in the pre-Albian and thus the fault may have acted as a growth fault.

At Fault Corner the Junction Bed on the west side of the fault is close to the Boueti Bed (at the base of the Forest Marble) on the downthrown side. Above the Boueti Bed follow the varied lithologies of the Forest Marble (Holloway 1983) with distinctive trace fossils (Hallam 1970, Ensom 1984a) which can be examined in the upper part of the cliff and in cliff falls.

The underlying Fuller's Earth clays can be examined from the shore in the cliffs to the east. Limestone reefs of the brachiopod-rich Wattonensis Beds are exposed, when the level of the shingle permits, some 170m east from Eype Mouth (see later). The name Frome Clay is sometimes used of the Upper Fuller's Earth between the Wattonensis Beds and the Boueti Bed.

6. WEST BAY

East from the Eype Mouth Fault Upper Lias and Middle Jurassic rocks are at shore level until the major Abbotsbury Fault is reached eight miles (12.8km) to the south-east (Fig. 5c–e). Accurate thickness measurements are often not possible, but the sequence comprises the Bridport Sands (44m), Inferior Oolite (27–42m), Fuller's Earth (44m+), Forest Marble (27–42m), Cornbrash (9m) and Oxford Clay (ca.120m). As in the west, Cretaceous rocks (Albian and younger) cap only the highest coastal hills. The rocks of the coast between Burton Cliff and Abbotsbury, being protected from sea erosion by the Chesil Beach, offer few exposures and are generally unrewarding to all but the specialist. Corresponding levels in most units are better exposed elsewhere.

6A. Watton Cliff (SY 456906). The car park on the West Esplanade (SY 459904) at West Bay gives access to Watton (or West) Cliff. Watton Cliff may be traversed at cliff top or shore level, given suitable tides, from Eype Mouth (see above). The traverse is here described from the west, where the

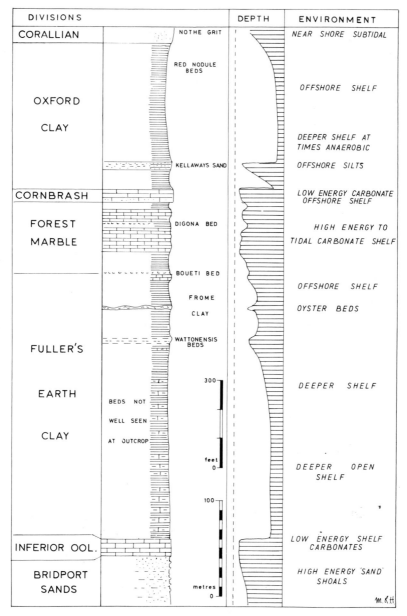

Figure 10.   The stratigraphical succession of the Middle Jurassic of the Dorset coast with an indication of possible depositional environments.

oldest beds seen east of the Eype Mouth Fault are the Wattonensis Beds, often seen cropping out through shingle at spring tides 170m east of Eype Mouth and against small faults further east. Known also as the Brachiopod Beds (*ca*. 7.6m) these show as a series of limestone beds dragged up against the fault at angles up to 75°. They contain a rich brachiopod fauna, including *Wattonithyris wattonensis*, *Rhynchonelloidella spp.*, *Rugitela bullata* and *Tubithyris* and others monographed by Muir-Wood (1936b). The level seems slightly younger than the Fuller's Earth Rock known to the north (Penn *et al.*, 1979). Overlying the Wattonensis Beds are oyster beds full of *Praeexogyra hebridica*. Some 25m of blue-grey marls of the Frome Clay (Upper Fuller's Earth Clay of usual terminology) are seen in the vertical cliffs west of the esplanade. At the base of the overlying Forest Marble is the Boueti Bed, and this is accessible at about 20m above OD by traversing the Dorset Cliff Path up the hill from the West Esplanade car park. *Goniorhynchia boueti* and other brachiopods and also bivalves are abundant and there are rare corals. Cream marly limestones below the Boueti Bed provide a marker in the cliffs. The overlying Forest Marble shows the distinctive fissile and coarse shell limestones indicative of increased current activity and of shallower water conditions.

6B. East Cliff (SY 464903). On the east side of West Bay it is possible to park close to the western end of East Cliff which exposes a superb sequence of the Bridport Sands (43m). Inaccessible Inferior Oolite and lower Fuller's Earth Clay are visible at the top of the higher parts of the cliff. The rhythmic alternation of hard (Plate 7) and soft bands in the Bridport Sands corresponds with alternations of carbonate-cemented and well-burrowed sands with rather uncemented and less burrowed sands. Crumpling of mica flakes in the latter and not in the former has been taken to indicate cementation took place soon after deposition and is said to be early diagenetic (Davies 1967) (Plate 7B). The well-cemented levels have been argued to be storm deposited (Bryant *et al.*, 1988) and are low in clay minerals and high in bioclasts. It has been argued that permeability was higher enabling early cementation by fringing cements. The environment of formation is thought to be turbulent and the substrate firm. By contrast the poorly-cemented levels are richer in clay minerals and poorer in bioclasts and are thought to be deposited under less turbulent conditions with a relatively soft substrate. The environment of formation would indicate an offshore sand shoal and some of the lower parts of the sequence show signs of marked storm activity (Plate 6C). Higher in the succession the rhythmic units become thinner as the Inferior Oolite is approached.

The Upper Lias sands, such as the Bridport Sands, extend north to the Cotswolds but faunas show that they young progessively southwards. This is a classic case of diachroneity, the Cotswold, Yeovil and Bridport Sands younging southward. In southern Dorset this facies extends into the Aalenian, indeed it is said to be mostly Aalenian in the Wytch Farm borehole but this probably results from the lack of good age markers in the early part of the Bridport Sand there. The Upper Lias sands represent a southwardly extending basinal infill which eventually gave the broad sand flats on which developed the carbonate shelf of the

Inferior Oolite. It is part of the model of major Jurassic rhythms that deepening is followed by gradual infilling and shallowing but this is the only level where the expected diachroneity of the sand units can be demonstrated.

7. BURTON BRADSTOCK

This is the best area (Fig. 11) along the coast for studying the Inferior Oolite but the Bridport Sands are also very well exposed as are parts of the lower Fuller's Earth. The Inferior Oolite is a remarkably condensed topmost Aalenian and Bajocian carbonate sequence in which a detailed ammonite biostratigraphy has enabled documentation of facies changes in the area south of the Mendips. Details for the Dorset area are given in the *Memoir* (Wilson *et al.*, 1958) which summarises the extensive earlier work of S.S. Buckman and L. Richardson. The best other exposures of the Inferior Oolite are inland. Horn Park Quarry (SY 458022) (Senior *et al.*, 1970) shows a development of Concavum and Murchisonae Zones. At Upton Farm (SY 512936), 390m north-west of Matravers, is a rather overgrown section passing from the top Bridport Sand to the lower Burton Limestone (Senior *et al.*, 1970). On the A35 east of Bridport there is an excellent section at Stony Head Cutting (SY 496927), 3.4km east of Bridport, which was described in detail by Parsons (1975).

7A. Burton Lane (SY 487892). There is very limited parking here. South from Burton Bradstock village the Bridport Sands are seen behind a garage (SY 487983) and the topmost part of the Sands and all of the Inferior Oolite is exposed and accessible in the lane leading south to the cliff top: these are the best localities for a short visit. After an examination of the sequence *in situ* here, where collecting is not possible, one is advised to go to the next locality (SY 479893), thc western end of Burton Cliff near Burton Freshwater, where detailed examination and collecting is possible from fallen blocks. The following sequence (Richardson 1928) is for the lane cutting (SY 487892):

UPPER BAJOCIAN
    Burton Limestone (top Beds) with
        Truelli Bed (0.6m) at base .... seen to 2.0m
    Astarte Bed 0.3–0.6
LOWER BAJOCIAN
    Red Conglomerate : 0–0.14
    Red Bed 0.8
    Snuff-Box Bed 0.1–0.2
AALENIAN
    Yellow Conglomerate 0–1.0
    Scissum Beds 0.5
    Bridport Sands (pars) 2.0
TOARCIAN
    Bridport Sands below

The top 2.0m of the Bridport Sand carry the small, rather smooth and discoidal ammonite *Leioceras opalinum*, the lowest Aalenian zone fossil, and hence belong in the Middle Jurassic. The Scissum Beds have the subzonal *Tmetoceras scissum*

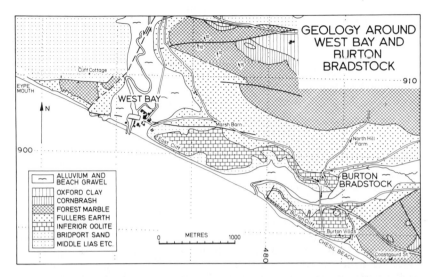

GEOLOGY AROUND
WEST BAY AND
BURTON
BRADSTOCK

ALLUVIUM AND
BEACH GRAVEL
OXFORD CLAY
CORNBRASH
FOREST MARBLE
FULLERS EARTH
INFERIOR OOLITE
BRIDPORT SAND
MIDDLE LIAS ETC.

Figure 11.   Geological map of the West Bay—Burton Bradstock area (after Wilson *et al.*, 1958).

(with strong ribbing disjunct over the venter). The Yellow Conglomerate marks a significant non-sequence with the zones of *Ludwigia murchisonae* and *Graphoceras concavum* here missing. The Snuff-Box (Plate 8A,B) is dated as belonging to the Zone of *Hyperliocera discites* of the basal Bajocian and is formed of limonite-concretions of algal stromatolitic laminations centred around bivalve shells and other nuclei (Gatrall *et al.*, 1972, Radley 1986, Palmer and Wilson 1990). The Red Conglomerate is a remanié bed of the Zone of *Stephanoceras humphresianum* but perhaps also of the earliest part of the Zone of *Strenoceras subfurcatum* above (otherwise missing). The Red Beds comprise the Zone of *Emileia sauzei* (layer A) and late Zone of *Witchelllia laeviuscula* (Level B) with the early part represented by a non-sequence.

The Astarte Bed belongs to the uppermost part of the zone of *Strenoceras garantiana*. The marked discontinuity below corresponds to the Vesulian transgression of earlier terminology. The Truelli Bed represents the Zone of *Parkinsonia parkinsoni*. The Burton Limestone has abundant sponges and bryozoa but these are best seen in fallen blocks below the cliffs. A famous locality for the level is Peashill Quarry at Shipton Gorge, 3.2km south-west of Bridport (SY 495916) described by Richardson (1928) and Walter (1967).

7B. Burton Cliff West (SY 483893). The fine cliff sections of Burton Cliff are best approached either from the Freshwater Caravan Park (SY 477896), or from the lane south of Burton Bradstock (above) and by walking west along the clifftop path to make a descent at the western end of the cliff after noticing the Inferior Oolite/Fuller's Earth junction exposed in the cliff top by a fault (Fig. 5d).

Only the top 40m of the Bridport Sands are seen in the cliffs. They comprise regular alternations of hard (more calcareous and cemented) and soft sands in an ABAB rhythmic pattern as at East Cliff. Evidence of burrowing organisms is prominent and trace fossils are abundant; hence most primary lamination has been destroyed by bioturbation. Apart from the top two metres these sands belong to the late Toarcian Levesquei Zone and upper subzones only of that. In the middle of the cliff, and at the base of it, are large scale cross-bedding structures, the only evidence of really strong current activity.

Along the shore below the cliffs, are often many fallen blocks of the Inferior Oolite which form the best locality to study the units outlined above and for fossil collection. There is a fascinating variety of facies for examination and there are significant small-scale variations in thickness of individual beds which yield a rich and varied fauna (Richardson 1928–1930). Every unit of the lane section can be examined and the Snuff Boxes (Plate 8A,B) are especially spectacular.

7C. Burton Cliff East (SY 491887). There is a National Trust car park at the end of Beach Road (SY 491889) and east of Burton Villas. West of the car park the Bridport Sands are again exposed in vertical cliffs. The Bride Fault disturbs the Bridport Sands where the path climbs to the cliff top to the west. Associated with the fault are white limestones which may indicate the presence of a contemporary fissue (neptunian dyke) of Bajocian date within the Bridport Sands (Richardson 1928–30). The Bride Fault belt downthrows 60m south and introduces the Middle Jurassic to the east (Plate 9A).

About 200m to the east of the car park the Boueti Bed can be traced in eroded ground between the footpath and the cliff top and it yields the brachiopods *Goniorhynchia boueti*, *Avonothyris*, *Digonella*, with bivalves and other fossils. In the cliffs below, the upper part of the Fuller's Earth Clay can be examined and it crops out in the low cliffs at Burton Common and Cliff End (SY 499883).

The cliffs to the south-east towards the Abbotsbury Fault (Figs. 5d, 5e) are much receded, landslipped and overgrown and are not particularly favourable for examination. However, fossiliferous outcrops of the Forest Marble were recorded by Sylvester-Bradley (1957).

II SOUTH DORSET COAST

The northern margin of the Weymouth lowlands is marked geologically by the Ridgeway Fault and the Abbotsbury Fault which is along the same line to the west. The east-west axis of the Weymouth Anticline passes through the middle of the Weymouth lowlands (Figs. 1, 12, block diagram on back cover). Fuller's Earth Clay and Forest Marble form the core rocks of the fold at outcrop and boreholes at Sea Barn Farm (SY 62638054) and in offshore West Bay (Dingwall and Lott 1979) give evidence of older beds. The core is much cut by east-west faults probably of both pre-Albian and Tertiary age. Dips in the Portland and Purbeck Beds of the Portesham to Upwey ridge dip 10°–20° north and, when traced to the west are unconformably overlain by Gault (Albian) in a way which shows that much of this dip is pre-Albian in date. Dips in the Corallian ridge at Wyke Regis are only about 5° south, and on Portland the general dip is 1.5° to the southeast.

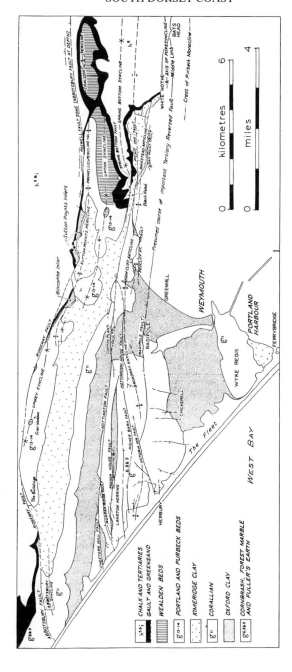

Figure 12.   Map illustrating the geological structure of the Weymouth area (after House 1961).

8. ABBOTSBURY, PORTESHAM AND DORCHESTER

The Abbotsbury Fault near Abbotsbury brings Upper Jurassic rocks down to the south against the Middle Jurassic rocks which form the hills from Burton Bradstock to Abbotsbury Hill. The fault at present has a throw of 180–210m to the south and is pre-Albian in age. To judge from its mapped course northwest of Abbotsbury Castle (Fig. 13), it has a significant southward dip. Eastward the fault passes into the Tertiary Ridgeway Fault at Portesham Withy Bed (SY 593859) (House 1961) so the Ridgeway Fault is demonstrably a reactivation of the Abbotsbury Fault. The present throw north of the Ridgeway Fault may be less than the pre-Albian throw south of the Abbotsbury Fault (Fig. 12). On the hills around the Abbotsbury Hill Fort to the north, Gault rests unconformably on the Forest Marble and the slopes below are heavily landslipped. Upper Greensand, Chalk and Bagshot Beds succeed on the high ground to the north-east.

8A. Abbotsbury (SY 576853). The sequence in the Abbotsbury area comprises the Oxford Clay (*ca.* 120m), Corallian Beds (*ca.* 45m), Abbotsbury Sandstone (8m), Abbotsbury Iron Ore (8m), Kimmeridge Clay (340m) Portland Beds (42m) and Purbeck Beds (67m), the last two being seen farther inland east of Portesham. The east-west axis of the Abbotsbury Syncline passes through the village centre where the youngest rocks are low in the Kimmeridge Clay and have yielded the ammonite *Aulacostephanus* in trenches. To the east, near Portesham (SY 602854) are old prospect workings for the Kimmeridge Oil Shale or Blackstone.

The Corallian and lower Kimmeridge Clay successions differ from the coastal sequence which is seen at Osmington Mills (Itinerary 12c). Little work has been done in the Corallian sequence here but there is a good quarry in the Osmington Oolite on Linton Hill (at SY 580847) and another (at SY 586847) in the Trigonia Beds and showing Sandsfoot Grit above. Brookfield (1978) has argued that the Sandsfoot Grit proper (up to middle Pseudocordata Zone) of the coast, is here absent and its place taken by what he calls the Abbotsbury Sandstone (8m, late Pseudocordata and Baylei Zones) which he considers to be equivalent to the Ringstead Waxy Clay. The immediately overlying Abbotsbury Ironstone (8m) is a chamosite oolitic quartz sandstone with interbeds of chamosite-siderite mudstone formerly worked for iron. Much of the chamosite is now weathered to limonite. Ooliths usually have quartz grains at their centre (Plate 17A). All outcrops are oxidised and the Ironstone is red in colour except when seen in deep trenches in the village when it appears green due to the natural colour of the iron silicate mineral chamosite. The Abbotsbury Ironstone carries a rich benthonic fauna, suggesting no lack of sea-floor aeration, including several brachiopod genera (Sandy 1985b), gastropods and serpulid worm tubes. Coarsely-ribbed ammonites of the early Kimmeridgian genus, *Rasenia* occur. Brookfield (1973) interprets the environment of formation as an offshore beach or barrier bar.

Virtually all the narrow lanes leading north from the main street at Abbotsbury show sections through deeply-weathered Abbotsbury Ironstone, especially Coward's Lane (SY 571856) and Red Lane (SY 575855), but Blind Lane, from 180m east of the school, leads up beside Jubilee Coppice (SY 576856) to a fine

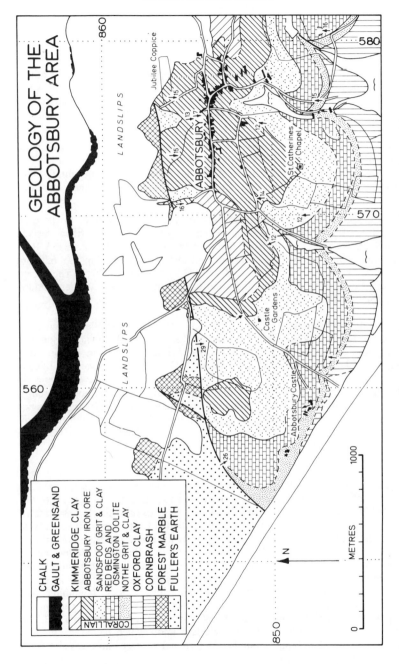

Figure 13.   Geological map of the Abbotsbury area. (In part after Wilson *et al.*, 1958.)

overview of the Abbotsbury Syncline. This locality has produced a good fauna with *Rasenia* and also bivalves, gastropods and brachiopods.

8B. Portesham (SY 603859). In the stream which passes through Portesham (or Portisham) village, especially between the Half Moon Inn and the Church, are large blocks of silicified gravels often called puddingstones or sarsens which are well developed near the base of the Tertiary hereabouts. For a discussion on the origin of sarsens see Summerfield (1979) and Summerfield and Jones (1980, in Jones (Ed.)).

East of Portesham is a quarry in the Portland Stone and Purbeck Beds (SY 609859) with a large silicified conifer trunk from the Fossil Forest level on the quarry floor. There is evidence of evaporites and of fluctuating salinity in the Lower Purbeck Beds here and the Charophyte Chert Bed has been identified (Barker *et al.*, 1975) associated with a rich flora and fauna.

From the Unio Bed of the Upper Purbeck in a quarry 1400m to the east-northeast (at SY 621865) West and Hooper (1969) have described derived Portland cherts and phosphatised Kimmeridgian fossils. The Portland Beds themselves, which are well seen farther east at the Coryates Gap (SY 630856) and Corton Gap (SY 637855), were described by Townson (1975). These gaps are responsible for the capture of the water table from the now dry Friar Waddon Valley (Sparks 1951).

8C. Hardy's Monument (SY 613876). On clear days the Blackdown ridge provides a fine overview of the whole of the Weymouth lowlands south to Portland and south-east to the cliffs beyond White Nothe. The monument is named after Nelson's ("kismet" or "kiss me" Hardy) naval friend who lived at Portesham and not the Dorset novelist. Quarries around are in gravels (about 9m thick) thought to be equivalent of the Bagshot Beds (Bournemouth Group), mostly of flint cobbles but with a range of Cornubian type Hercynian lithologies and of late Jurassic and Cretaceous Upper Greensand cherts. Bronkham Down, to the south-east is famous for its Bronze Age burial mounds and for some 200 solution subsidence hollows, or dolines (House 1992).

8D. Maiden Castle (SY 664887). The car park for this Ancient Monument is at the end of Maiden Castle Road to the north of the spectacular western entrance but a car can be parked along the narrow road near the eastern entrance (SY 674879) west of Winterbourne Monkton. Said to have the largest area of defences of any Iron Age hill-fort in Europe, Maiden Castle lies 3km south-west of Dorchester on a double knoll. It was originally excavated by Sir Mortimer Wheeler between 1933 and 1938, and more recently in 1985 and 1986 by English Heritage. Wheeler thought it might have been the ancient city of Danium referred to by Ptolemy. It would have been a major centre for the local tribes, the Durotriges, when the Romans arrived but has a long history, beginning over 5000 years ago. The visible earthworks originated as a single rampart on the eastern knoll, completed by about 500 BC. In the late 3rd Century BC, the defences were extended to enclose the western knoll which increased the area occupied to about 189,000m^2. Complex eastern and western entrances and outer earthworks were developed before the final remodelling around 100 BC. About 44 AD, the Legio II Augusta is thought to have taken the hill-fort, but native occupation was allowed to continue. Hoards totalling over 54,000 slingstones have been recovered, mostly originating from the Chesil Beach. A late 4th Century temple is visible (SY 671885), built of a herring-bone flintwork above levelling courses of Purbeck stone.

8E. Dorset County Museum (SY 692907). On High West Street at Dorchester is the museum of the Dorset Natural History and Archaeological Society. It is a quite admirable museum made especially famous by the archaeological remains, particularly those from Maiden Castle, and by the fine collection of well-exhibited Dorset fossils. It also contains memorabilia of Thomas Hardy (1840–1928) the novelist who was born at Higher Bockhampton (SY 728925), lived at Max Gate 1.5km southeast of Dorchester, and whose heart is buried at Stinsford Church (SY 712910) (other remains are in Poet's Corner at Westminster Abbey).

9. FLEET SHORE

Worth-while localities are scattered, and it seems best to describe them in stratigraphic order (Figs. 12, 14). The beds seen range from Fuller's Earth to Oxford Clay. Doornkamp (1964) has described the landform development of this area. Permission to visit the northern part of the Fleet shore should be sought from the Strangways Estate Warden, Fallowhide, Rodden (Tel. (0305) 871242). For Herbury permission should be obtained from the farmer, Manor Farm House, Stourton Caundle, Sherborne (Tel. (0963) 62471). Access to the southern Fleet shore is provided by the Dorset Coastal Path. There are no convenient paths to the northern localities.

9A. Rodden Hive Point (SY 599821). The oldest beds exposed are near Rodden Hive Point and are clays with mudstones with the bivalves *Nucula* and *Myophorella* and crushed ammonites, especially *Procerites* (Arkell 1947, House 1957) often with attached worm tubes and bryozoa. These are beds of the Fuller's Earth and the level is thought to be equivalent to the Wattonensis Beds but the brachiopod *Wattonithyris* has not been recorded. The Wattonensis Beds were proved to be 32m below the Hebridica Beds in the Sea Barn Farm Borehole with 185m of Fuller's Earth below down to the Inferior Oolite.

9B. Langton Hive Point (SY 606814). The Point is best approached by a private track from Langton Herring (Fig. 14) at the end of which is a small car park. The Hebridica Beds of the Fuller's Earth crop out in a low cliff a few metres north from where the track reaches the shore and are here some 5m thick, but map inland as thickening and thinning as expected for oyster banks (House 1961). They are an oyster shell bank (lumachelle) full of *Praeexogyra hebridica* s.s. and var. *elongata*, often encrusted with minute attached foraminiferans including *Nubeculinella. Radulopecten* and crushed rhynchonellids also occur.

9C. Herbury (SY 611810). The Boueti Bed, at the base of the Forest Marble, with the uppermost Fuller's Earth below is exposed near the north-west tip of Herbury. The fauna includes the brachiopods *Goniorhynchia boueti*,

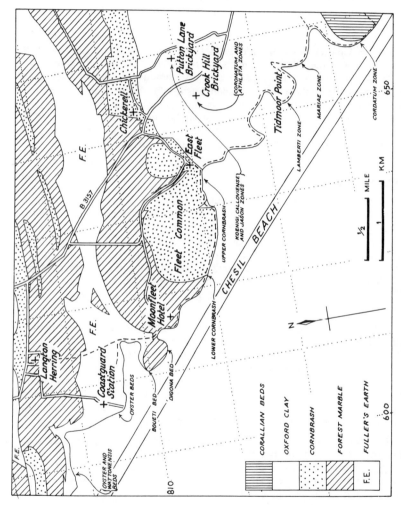

Figure 14.   Map of the shore of the Fleet showing localities of interest (modified from
House 1969).

Cyrtorhynchia, Avonothyris, Digonella, Dictyothyris and many bivalves and microfossils. Ammonites and echinoids are rare. It is now almost collected out. The fauna may be collected all along the considerable outcrop inland, especially in fields under plough (see detailed map in House 1961). Full faunal lists were given by Richardson (1909) and Fowler (1957) and microfossils have been studied by Sylvester-Bradley (1948) and Cifelli (1959). The bed may be traced to just north of the Mendips. The similarity over so wide an area suggests a pause in sedimentation enabling suspension-feeding brachiopods to flourish. The small faults at Herbury have been said to be contemporary with deposition (Lake 1986a) because the successions differ across the faults. Slight wrench movements could produce the same results.

There are no good quarries in the Forest Marble but many of the stone walls of the lowlands are of shelly flags from the upper division which are readily collected from fields under plough (Plate 9C, 10B). There are good exposures in the low cliffs of Herbury and on the foreshore to near Moonfleet Hotel (SY 617805). Near the southern end of Herbury the Digona Bed crops out. This level overlies the main flaggy division and the cream and grey marls have common *Digonella digona, Avonothyris, Dictyothyris, Rhynchonelloidea*, and the crinoid, *Apiocrinites*, with well-preserved bivalves. In the Sea Barn Farm (SY 626805) borehole 75m of Forest Marble was proved.

9D. Shipmoor Point (SY 576836). This is the best local exposure of the Cornbrash but it is unfortunately difficult of access and permission is required from the Strangways Estate. It can be approached on foot from a bend in the road between Rodden and Abbotsbury (SY 589834). There are 6.5m exposed including the very fossiliferous Lower Cornbrash (2m) with the zonal guide brachiopods *Cererithyris intermedia* below and *Obovithyris obovata* above: other brachiopods include *Kallirhynchia yaxleyensis* and the bivalves *Meleagrinella echinata, Pleuromya, Pholadomya, Ctenostreon* and others. The more massive limestones of the Upper Cornbrash follow and yield the brachiopods *Rhynchonelloidella cerealis, Microthyridina siddingtonensis* and the large burrowing bivalve *Pholadomya deltoidea*. The ammonite *Clydoniceras* is expected from the Lower Cornbrash and *Macrocephalites* from the Upper Cornbrash. Douglas and Arkell (1928) have illustrated many of the faunal elements. The widespread nature of Cornbrash facies in England and the abundance of suspension-feeding benthos suggest a period of warm, shallow seas with very little clastic input from neighbouring land areas.

A similar section to that at Shipmoor Point is seen at Berry Knap (SY 586830) 1.1 km to the southeast where the Cornbrash dips 15° to the north.

The rich fauna of the Cornbrash is readily collected wherever the level is under plough, as often immediately north of the Langton Herring road (around SY 621824) where Forest Marble rubble strews the field to the south and the boundary runs along the road. The Upper Cornbrash yielded *Macrocephalites* on the Fleet shore in Butterstreet Cove near Fleet (SY 630791-634791) which is easy of access by the footpath to the shore past the isolated church. Faunas of the Lower Cornbrash can sometimes be found farther west. In the Sea Barn Farm Borehole 18.2m of Cornbrash was proved.

9E. Putton Lane (SY 650797). Outcrops of the Kellaways Beds and Oxford Clay (perhaps 250m thick) are now very poor except at Jordan or Furzy Cliff (Itinerary 12A) which expose only the upper parts. The Kellaways Beds can now hardly be traced at the defunct Putton Lane Brickyard. Brickmaking stopped here in 1965 and currently the site is being turned into a housing estate. Similarly the old brickpit at Bockenhampton is filled in (SY 474915). Similar levels on the Fleet shore (SY 635797-642791) described by Arkell (1948) are also poorly exposed and are not recommended.

The lower Oxford Clay in the area, being high in organic material was generally dug for brickmaking, but all pits are now abandoned. The most anoxic levels are within the Callovian and precede the international deepening at that level associated with the Callovian transgression.

9F. Crook Hill (SY 644797). The old brickyard here formerly exposed the Coronatum and Athleta Zones superbly but is now degraded. The white micritic casts of the noded body chambers of *Peltoceras athleta* from the upper 5m can sometimes be found, and there are crushed spinose kosmoceratid ammonites, bivalves and gastropods in the shales. Rare reineckiid ammonites (with a smooth band on the venter), and occasional fish remains, such as *Heterostrophus* and *Leptolepis*, have been found, as has the rare teuthoid, *Geopeltis* (Carreck 1960). Brickmaking stopped here in 1969.

9G. Tidmoor Point (SY 643787). This locality is on the foreshore dangerously behind the firing range. The highest part of the Callovian and the Middle Oxford Clay are poorly exposed here especially after winter storms. Pyritic ammonites of the Lamberti Zone were formerly abundant, especially *Quenstedtoceras lamberti* (with sickle-shaped ribs chevroned over the venter), *Kosmoceras* (spiny and noded) and *Peltoceras*.

9H. Furzedown (SY 646784). Oxford Clay of the lowest Oxfordian Mariae Zone crops out very poorly on the promontory to the south Tidmoor Point. The pyritic ammonite fauna has the more rotund *Quenstedtoceras*, *Q. mariae*, and also early cardioceratids (developing a weak keel). This unpromising exposure is the type section for the Furzedown Clays (see Itinerary 12A).

9I. Lynch Cove (SY 646781). The uppermost parts of the Oxford Clay, including the Red Nodule Beds occur around here with the ammonite *Cardioceras* and giant incurved oyster *Gryphaea dilatata*. The Dorset Coast Path provides a right of way on the Fleet cliff top above all these Oxford Clay localities. Faunas were listed by Arkell (1947) in the *Memoir*.

10. WYKE REGIS

The Corallian Beds are well exposed on both sides of the Wyke Regis promontory and there are footpaths virtually all the way along the cliffs. It is more sensible to visit these localities after seeing the more spectacular developments between Bowleaze Cove and Ringstead (Itinerary 12 : see Fig. 20 for a guide to the Corallian units and also Wright 1986a). The localities are listed from west to east.

10A. Camp Road (SY 652772). The Fleet shore here is best approached by following Camp Road 1.4 km southwest from Wyke Church (SY 662778). At the Fleet shore (at SY 652772), the Nothe Grits are seen west of the Coastguard Station (SY 648776) and the Bencliff Grit where Camp Road meets the shore : then there are good exposures of the Osmington Oolite (seen to a thickness of at least 16m) for 500m to the southeast.

10B. Ferry Bridge (SY 666763). Higher levels of the Corallian and the lowest Kimmeridge Clay are best approached from near the site of the old bridge (Ferry Bridge, or Small Mouth). The low cliffs to the northwest, and the foreshore beyond the first promontory, can make good collecting in the Ringstead Waxy Clay to basal Lower Kimmeridge Clay. The flat oyster, *Deltoideum delta*, the ribbed bivalve *Ctenostreon*, and the small coiled oyster *Nanogyra* and ammonites of the genus *Pictonia* are especially well-known from here. The twisted worm tube *Cycloserpula intestinalis* is common. A similar succession to that at Ringstead can be worked out. Sandsfoot Grit forms the promontory to the north-west (at SY 658767).

10C. Sandsfoot Cove (SY 676774). This is readily approached by road from Weymouth and there are steps down to the shore 450m south of the dog-leg turn on the A354 at Rodwell. This descent at Castle Cove shows, to the east, Western Ledges of Osmington Oolite followed by Trigonia Beds full of *Myophorella* and *Gervillella*. The Sandsfoot Clay is seen on the south side of the Cove and the Sandsfoot Grits with *Pinna sandsfootensis* crop out around the Sandsfoot Castle promontory and may be approached from Castle Cove or by descending from the Gardens there.

The coast at the southern end of Rylands Lane (SY 672772) may be reached from the A 354 by the Lane or by continuing along the road past Sandsfoot Castle (built by Henry VIII) and along the shore. Ledges of the Sandsfoot Grit extend along the cliffs to the south of Rylands Lane (SY 672772) and there the succeeding Ringstead Waxy Clays, rich in *Deltoideum delta*, and Ringstead Coral Bed can be traced in the low cliffs but tipping from a development at the cliff top east of the old railway bridge has made this difficult. Lower Kimmeridge Clay levels, often badly slipped, can be seen in the low cliffs towards Ferry Bridge and these have been a source of many reptile remains (Delair 1986).

10D. The Nothe (SY 686787). Here, south of Weymouth Harbour, the Nothe Grits are well exposed beside the walk along the south side of the harbour to the headland. Dredging in the harbour nearby has yielded ammonites of the Red Nodule Beds (House 1955). Exposures of Nothe Grit also occur on the southern side of the promontory, especially as a result of recent slipping, and in Newton's Cove (SY 683785) and there are paths and ornamental gardens around the headland giving access (Wright 1986a).

11. PORTLAND

The peninsula of Portland exposes Kimmeridge Clay to the north followed by the Portland Beds and lower Purbeck Beds which dip with a gentle dip of about 1.5° to the southsoutheast. The Portland Beds are cut by conjugate joints and master

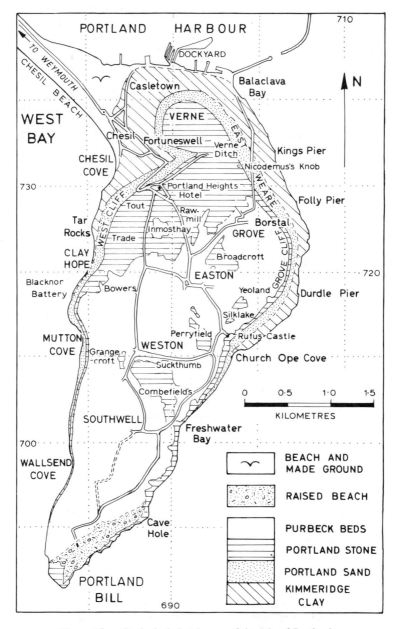

Figure 15. Geological sketch-map of the Isle of Portland.

joints but are not faulted. There is much evidence of ancient landslipping around the coast.

Portland (Fig. 15) has virtually a continuous rock exposure along the coasts and, as a result of quarrying, over much of the surface of the island. Portland Stone is probably the most famous English building stone. It is highly durable, and is an excellent freestone, capable of being cut in any direction. Extraction from quarries makes use of the well-developed master joints. Portland Stone owed its reputation first to the introduction of the stone to London by Inigo Jones in the reconstruction of the Banqueting Hall in Whitehall, but especially because Sir Christopher Wren used it, almost exclusively, for the many buildings and churches built after the Great Fire of London in 1666. An account of the quarrying methods has been given by Hounsell (1952, 1962). Portland quarrymens' terms have been reviewed by Arkell (1945).

The three localities described below enable the succession to be followed through completely, and will serve as a guide at other localities.

The Kimmeridge Clay is known down to the Blackstone or Oil Shale level but is not permanently exposed on the island. The Portland Beds are about 64.5m thick and the 30m of the overlying Purbeck Beds may just reach the Cretaceous Durlston Beds since loose fragments of the Cinder Bed are known near Southwell. A generalised section of the sequence is shown in an accompanying diagrams (Figs. 16, 17). The most recent account, incidental to a broader study, is by Townson (1975) who introduces a new terminology, not related to the new facies divisions he recognises but essentially replacement names for the terms and units well described and discriminated by Arkell (1947). The sequence is as follows with Townson's terms in parenthesis:

PORTLAND STONE
    Portland Freestone (Winspit Member) 9.0m
    Cherty Series 15.0
    Basal Shell Bed 2.7
        (the last two comprising the Dancing Ledge and
        Dungy Head Members)

PORTLAND SAND
    Portland Clay 4–6.0
    West Weare Sandstone 15.0
        (These two together comprising the Gad Cliff
        Member)
    Cast Beds (Pondfield Member) 1.3
    Exogyra Beds (Corton Hill Member) 7.5
    Upper Black Nore Beds 12.0
    Black Nore Sandstone 2.0
    Lower Black Nore beds

KIMMERIDGE CLAY (below)
    Lower Black Nore Beds below (all the three units of the
    Black Nore Beds Townson refers to the Black Nore
    Member)

Townson (1975) was the first to recognise that the so-called sandstones are usually silt-grade dolomites and he envisaged the dolomitisation to be sub-tidal and original. He also recognised several distinct limestone facies here and on the Isle of Purbeck. The six facies are :

FACIES 1. Lime mudstone : micrite with less than 10% of grains other than faecal pellets

FACIES 2. Spicule wackestone : micrite with more than 10% grains of which 60–70% are the spherical, originally siliceous spicules of rhaxellid sponges, preserved now as calcite casts (Plate 12C).

FACIES 3. Fine bioclast packstone : well-sorted bioclast sand with spicules, serpulids and bivalves common (Plate 12B).

FACIES 4. Bioclast grainstone : sparite-cemented medium to coarse bivalve fragment sand.

FACIES 5. Ooid grainstone : poor to well-sorted ooids with sparite cement (Plate 23).

FACIES 6. Bivalve shell-grainstone to -packstone: grain-supported whole or fragmented bivalves with lime sand or mud matrix.

Facies 1 is the 'chalky' facies of the Portland Stone inland (as at Chalbury Quarry (SY 693837), Itinerary 14D). Facies 2 is best illustrated by the Cherty Series where the silica of the sponges has concentrated as chert nodules during diagenesis. Facies 3 and 4 characterise the Portland Stone east of the supposed swell area of Lulworth whilst Facies 5 characterises the Lulworth and Portland development and occurs in the Purbeck sequences as discrete beds. Townson considered Lulworth to Portland was the swell line on which Facies 5 developed, but there is no evidence for joining these areas and they could well have been independent shoal crests.

The early Purbeck Beds proceed through fossil soils and stromatolitic and calcareous tufa levels with tree trunks to hypersaline lagoon facies micrites and faecal pellet limestones. There is a level of sub-globular stromatolites 12.2m above the base (House 1968) seen at the top of the 'overburden' in many of the southern quarries : this level is also maintained in Purbeck. Stromatolitic algae or, in more modern terms, Cyanobacteria, by analogy with those of present-day freshwater lakes could be the source of much of the fine micrite and marl of the Purbeck Beds. Finely dispersed calcite rhombs are common in interstitial spaces in both the Portland Stone and early Purbeck here and show well under the scanning electron microscope.

11A. Tar Rocks (SY 681725). From a car park south of Portland Square near Brandy Row (SY 683733) a coastal footpath leads southsouthwest to Tar Rocks 950m away below West Weare Cliffs (Plate 20). The landslip section here (Fig. 16) shows Kimmeridge Clay beneath boulders at low water and then a sequence of buff-weathering dolomitic silts with doggers of the Lower Black Nore Beds with the ammonite *Virgatopavlovia* below and *Progalbanites* (or *Zaraiskites*) in the uppermost part and in the massive Blacknore Sandstone above. Just above the massive beds is a level with the brachiopod *Rhynchonella* s.s. The Kimmeridgian/Portlandian boundary is drawn between the Zones of

Virgatopavlovia fittoni and *Progalbanites albani* and here lies within the foreshore exposures. The Black Nore Sandstone is full of rhaxellid sponge spicules, illustrated on Plate 12C (Haslett 1992).

One hundred metres south of Tar Rocks the landslip section gives a full section through the Portland Stone. The lowest Purbeck section above is the most easily accessible in the northern part of the island.

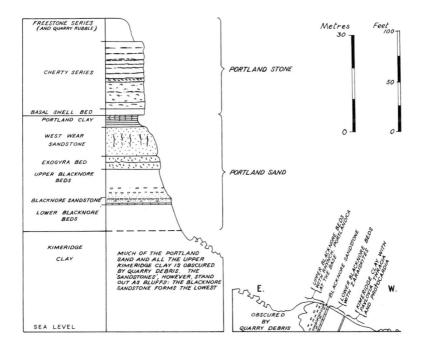

Figure 16.   Diagrammatic sections of the Portland Beds exposed along the West Weare Cliffs, Portland. On the left, immediately north of Blacknor Battery; on the right the landslip section at Tar Rocks. An alternative name for *Zaraiskites* is *Progalbanites* (modified from House 1958). Note the spelling of Kimmeridge with one 'm'. This was the style used in the Domesday Book and by D'Orbigny when naming the Kimeridgien stage. Note that Black Nore and Blacknor are alternative spellings although the former is commonly in geological use.

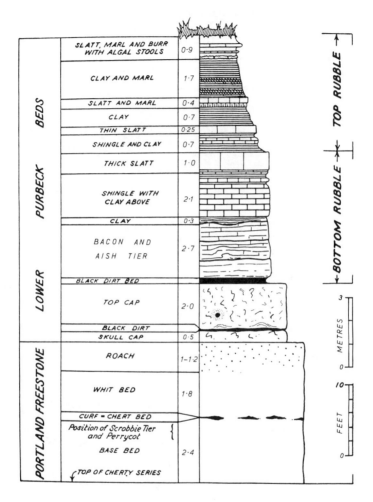

Figure 17.   Section of the beds exposed in Perryfield Quarry, Portland, showing the terms used by the quarrymen (after House 1958).

Higher levels can be examined in the bluffs below the cliffs at Blacknore Battery where the Exogyra Beds full of the oyster *Nanogyra nana* form a feature. The Portland Clay forms a recess below the cliffs and the Basal Shell Bed above is full of well-preserved bivalves and gastropods and abundant serpulids (see Cox 1925) and may be worked south into Mutton Cove. The good sections around Black Nore Battery are time-consuming to examine but there is usually a difficult route up to the cliff-top footpath which cannot be recommended.

11B.   Portland Heights Hotel (SY 688729). From the cliff top at Verne Yeates is a splendid view of the Chesil Beach and the Weymouth lowlands north to the Ridgeway. The former fossil garden of the Bath and Portland Stone Firms Ltd. has now been incorporated in the northern walls and gardens of the Hotel. There is a particularly fine conifer trunk, standing vertically near the hotel entrance.

11C.   Church Ope Cove (SY 696711). If the road to Easton is followed, bearing left through Easton Square, the rewarding Portland Museum (SY 695713) stands just beside the turn to the narrow road leading to the late 15th Century Rufus Castle, beneath the foundations of which and beside the steps to the shore is an excellent succession from the Cherty Series to the lowest Lulworth Beds.

11D.   Perryfield Quarry (SY 694712). Continuing west, and about 300m beyond the museum, this recently reopened quarry is on the north side of the road, just beyond Pennsylvania Castle. The succession is given in Fig. 17, and there is a lithological log given by West *et al.* (1969). The striking algal stools from near the top of the sequence range in diameter from a few cm to 0.5m diameter. Two types occur, one with serpulids and with mammilated irregular outer surfaces, the other without internal annelid tubes and smooth-surfaced. Similar stools form today in freshwater lakes and rivers in calcareous areas of England and Scotland (House 1968). The Portland Stone here yields fine masses of the red calcareous alga *Solenoporella* and also the bivalves *Laevitrigonia gibbosa*, *Myophorella incurva*, *Protocardia dissimilis*, *Camptonectes lamellosus* and *Pleuromya tellina* with the internal moulds of the turrited gastropod *Aptyxiella portlandica* (known as the Portland Screw). The stone for Waterloo Bridge came from here and adjacent quarries.

11E.   Freshwater Bay (SY 692703). This is the best place to study the Portland Limestone. A track near spot height 192 diverges from the Easton to Southwell road and leads, with parking, to an old cliff-top quarry in the Portland Beds and Lulworth Beds. The Top Cap of the early Purbeck Beds shows good algal-type laminations and convolutions and tree trunks with a dirt (soil) bed above (Francis 1983). An easy route down the cliff gives access to a complete section of the Cherty Series with the Basal Shell Bed (Plate 11B) well seen some 200m to the north-west. This has the serpulid worm *Glomerula gordialis* especially common (Plate 12B) and there is a level full of the large ammonite *Glaucolithites*.

11F.   Portland Bill (SY 677683). There is a large car park here, and good exposures of the Portland Stone and earliest Purbeck Beds. West of the lighthouse the Portland Raised Beach 7.6m above O.D. can be examined and it continues east for 1000m in the cliff top. The pebbles are mostly of local Mesozoic rocks but include granite, porphyry and Bunter quartzite pebbles. Davies and Keen (1985) distinguish an eastern beach (dated at 125,000 BP), visible in the coastal sections northeast of the lighthouse, and a western beach (dated at 210,000 BP), seen in the Admiralty property northwest of the lighthouse. The eastern beach yielded to them 62 molluscan species of rocky, near shore environments suggesting temperatures similar to the present. The western beach fauna included eight foraminiferan species and several molluscs. East from the lighthouse brecciated (and often rounded) limestones associated with

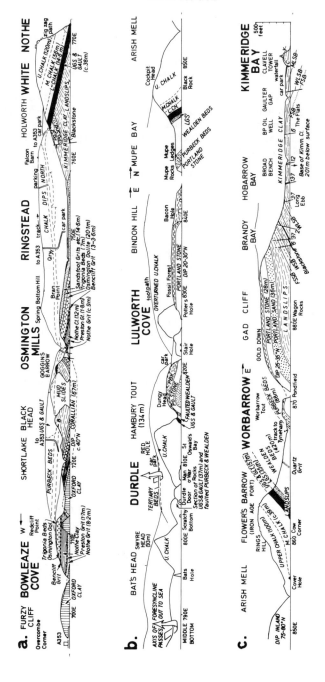

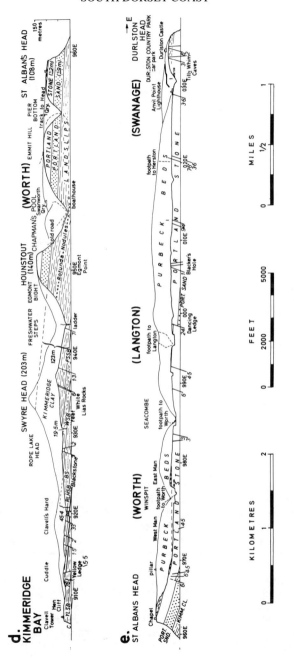

Figure 18.   Coastal sections of the South and East Dorset coast from Owermoigne Corner, 3.5km north-east of Weymouth, to Durlston Head, south of Swanage. Vertical exaggeration ×3.

the raised beach have been argued to be cryoturbation structures formed under permafrost conditions (Pugh and Shearman 1967, West *et al.* 1969).

12. BOWLEAZE COVE TO RINGSTEAD

Along the coast from Furzy Cliff (SY 697816) past Redcliff Point and Osmington Mills to Holworth House (SY 763816) (Fig. 18a) a full sequence from the upper Oxford Clay to the Purbeck Beds is visible. The beds are affected by east-west trending folds, such as the Ham Cliff Anticline (Plate 14B) and Ringstead Anticline, and various strike faults with some dip faults in the east. At White Nothe and above Black Head, southward dipping Gault unconformably overlies northward dipping Upper Jurassic and the Gault is in turn overlain by Upper Greensand and Chalk (Fig. 18, Plate 18A,B). The localities will be described from west to east and this follows the succession upwards from the oldest beds. Something of the interplay of Pre-Albian and Tertiary structures hereabouts has been already illustrated (Figs, 3, 4).

12A. Furzy Cliff (SY 697816-703819). The Upper Oxford Clay (45m exposed) of Furzy (or Jordan) Cliff can be approached either from car parks at the western end at Owermoigne Corner or from the east end at Bowleaze Cove (Fig. 18a). The Nothe Grit enters by the northward dip in the north part of Furzy Cliff, but there is a slight southern dip near Owermoigne Corner. The succession (Cope *et al.*, 1980, Wright 1986b) is as follows giving names used for subdivision of the Oxford Clay:

> CORALLIAN (pars)
>   Nothe Grit above
> OXFORD CLAY (pars)
>   Bowleaze Clay with Red Nodule
>   Bed 6m below top 12m
>   Jordan Cliff Clays .... 9+
>   Furzedown Clays (incompletely seen) ....? 18

The Bowleaze Clays are only seen in the central part of the cliff, below the capping of Nothe Grit, and they are in the Costicardia Subzone of the Zone of *Cardioceras cordatum*: the Jordan Cliff Clays are of the Bukowskii Subzone (the lowest). How much of the Furzedown Clay occurs here is uncertain. Only the Praecordatum Subzone is recorded. The type-locality of the Furzedown Clay is at Furzedown (Itinerary 9H). The Oxford Clay here is badly landslipped but the ammonite *Cardioceras*, the oysters *Gryphaea dilatata*, and *Lopha* and the calcareous worm tubes of serpulids are common at certain horizons. Ichthyosaurian, crocodile and crustacean remains are known from here.

12B. Redcliff Point (SY 712816). The cliffs east from the car park at Bowleaze Cove expose a full succession of the Corallian (Fig. 20, see details for Osmington Mills below). The lower Corallian is especially well seen here and has formed the basis for studies on palaeoecology and trace fossils (Fürsich, 1975, 1977). The Preston Grit shows the trace fossil burrows *Thalassinoides* and *Rhizocorallium*, and the burrowing bivalve *Pleuromya* occurs in life position.

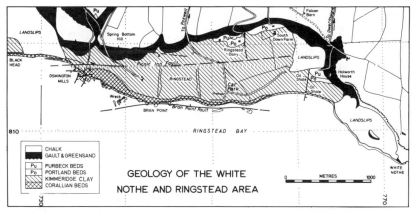

Figure 19.   Geological sketch map of the region around Osmington Mills, Ringstead and
              White Nothe.

From the Bencliff Grit the trace fossil *Asterosoma* in addition to *Diplocraterion*
has been recorded. Other faunal elements are recorded in the *Memoir* by Arkell
(1947).

Around Redcliff Point the Upper Oxford Clay is well seen, dipping 6°S and
faulted against the Corallian of the southern limb of the Ham Cliff Anticline and
it occurs again in the core of the Ham Cliff Anticline (Plate 11). Pyritized
ammonites of the Mariae Zone occur and those of the Lamberti Zone have been
recorded.

12C.   Osmington Mills (SY 734816). The stretch of coast between Black Head
and east of Bran Point (Plate 15) is most conveniently approached from the
private car park at Osmington Mills (SY 734817). The cliffs are particularly
celebrated for the excellent sections of the Corallian Beds (Arkell 1947, Wright
1986a) and of the Kimmeridge Clay (Ziegler 1962). In addition, the landslips east
of Black Head provide foundered blocks of the Cretaceous succession, especially
those showing the Cenomanian Basement Bed (formerly well seen *in situ* in a
quarry beside the Ringstead road at SY 747822).

For convenience sections of the Corallian given here (Fig. 19) are based on the
work of Arkell (1936) and Talbot (1973). Arkell's bed numbers will be referred
to since, despite much speculation on the sequence, his is still the only adequate
description. The unit terms have been brought up-to-date (Cope *et al.*, 1980).
Arkell took the view that the Corallian sequence hereabouts could be interpreted
in terms of three lithological rhythms, each comprising a sequence of clay,
sandstone and limestone. The Kimmeridge Clay he took to initiate an overlying
rhythm. The critical initiating units for Arkell's rhythms are as follows :

    4.   Kimmeridge Clay Bed 26
    3.   Sandsfoot Clay Bed 19
    2.   Nothe Clay Bed 12
    1.   Oxford Clay (initiated well below, see Fig. 20)

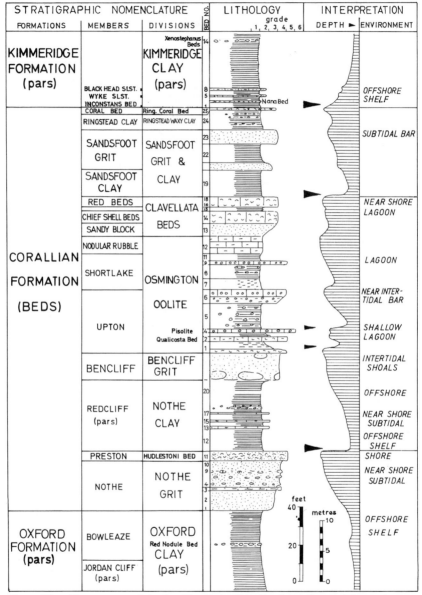

Figure 20.   The sequence of the Corallian Beds of the Bowleaze Cove to Ringstead area
              (modified from Arkell 1947 and Talbot 1971). Member terminology from
              Cox and Gallois (1981) and Wright (1986a, b).

This interpretation has been disputed by Talbot (1973) who, whilst accepting the general hypothesis, emphasises the regressive nature of the 'cycles' (as he prefers), and considers the limestones to initiate the 'cycles'. He considers the first two Corallian 'cycles' (2 and 3 below) to have initiated erosion levels which correlate with pebble beds inland. One additional rhythm results, but Arkell would have regarded this as a minor fluctuation on his scheme. The critical units initiating Talbot's 'cycles' are as follows :

5. Ringstead Coral Bed (Bed 25)
4. Sandy Block (Bed 13)
3. Basal Bed (Bed 1)
2. Trigonia hudlestoni Bed (now Preston Grit) (Bed 11)
1. Oxford Clay (as above)

It has been argued by Brookfield (1978) that the early Kimmeridge Clay itself represents an initial Kimmeridgian cycle and he resurrects the old term Passage Beds for this for levels from the Ringstead Waxy Clay up to a particular level in the Zone of *Rasenia cymodoce*. Torrens and Wright (in Cope *et al.*, 1980, p. 13−16) have attempted a more widespread analysis of the Corallian rhythms in relation to the claim that they are global and eustatic. Their conclusion is that erosion surfaces were commoner in the south of England than in Yorkshire and hence they prefer a local tectonic cause for some of the minor rhythms.

Sun (1989) has interpreted the local sequence in terms of four regressive−transgressive cycles in opposition to the usual view of asymmetric shallowing upward cycles (as on Fig. 20). However, the evidence linking maximum regression with inland pebble beds is important and difficult to reconcile with this view.

Valuable studies of Corallian faunas and facies have been published by Fürsich (1975, 1976, 1977) which are particularly helpful because he illustrates many of the fossils and especially the trace fossils (Fürsich 1975, p. 154). He uses the name *Spongeliomorpha* in place of *Thalassinoides*.

West of Osmington Mills the upper part of the Corallian and the lower Kimmeridge Clay is more conveniently studied in the northward dipping exposures east and west of the landslips between Black Head and Osmington Mills. On Black Head a full sequence of the Kimmeridge Clay from the basal beds to levels well above the White Stone Band can be examined. This is the type section of the Lower Kimmeridgian (Ziegler 1962). The beach below Black Head includes many green and grey concretions derived from the Upper Greensand which contain oysters, serpulids and echinoids. Purple-tinted concretions come from the base of the Gault and have yielded the ammonite *Hoplites* and other fossils.

East from the slipway south of the car park at Osmington Mills, Nothe Grit forms the low cliffs and these may be seen by descending the slipway seen from the car park and working east. There are huge doggers of the Bencliff Grit fallen from what appears to be a fault wedge higher in the cliff. At the Cascade (SY 736816) is a small waterfall over the Preston Grit (here 1.7m thick and with the bivalves *Pleuromya*, *Gryphaea* and *Myophorella hudlestoni*; the bed was formerly called the Hudlestoni Bed). There must be a fault displacement immediately east of the Cascade where there are landslips associated with the

Nothe Clay which is exposed east of the mudslides. Large doggers of the Bencliff Grit hereabouts show Fontainebleau texture and freshly broken surfaces show large matrix crystals which can glint in the sun. Also spectacular are the U-shaped burrows of *Diplocraterion parallelum* and slump structures. Beyond where the cliffs begin (Plate 15A) there are oil-sand levels in the upper part of the Bencliff Grit. These were some of the local oil seeps which stimulated the search for oil structures in the late 1930's.

The Qualicosta Bed (Bed 2) forms a prominent ledge west of Bran Point (Plate 15B), and at the Point the Bran Point Fault brings the Middle White Oolite (Bed 6) almost against the Pisolite (Bed 4, Plate 16B). A band in the Middle White Oolite is crowded with the U-shaped burrows of *Arenicolites variabilis* (see Fürsich 1975). From near Bran Point there is often a good view of White Nothe and the Pre-Albian unconformity.

Further east the succession may be followed up to the Trigonia Beds in the cliffs and there are many fallen blocks with *Myophorella clavellata*. Higher units are described under the next locality which can be reached by walking on east. Where the cliffs end there is a clamber to the cliff top path which enables a return to Osmington Mills where the Kimmeridge Clay, dipping at a high angle, is usually exposed in the stream 200m above the Smugglers Inn.

12D. Ringstead (SY 752814). A car park here is reached by toll road from the A352 south of Poxwell the narrow road passing through Upton and a sharp right turn at the top of the hill. The low cliffs hereabouts show intermittently the lowest 5m of the Kimmeridge Clay with the oyster *Deltoideum delta* in abundance: the ammonites *Rasenia* (with rather coarse ribs on inner whorls) and *Pictonia* have been recorded. At the base is a 0.3m bed full of the fingernail-sized oyster *Nanogyra nana*, and in a 0.6m unit of clay below (Bed 26) occurs the ammonites *Pictonia*, *Prorasenia*, and the bizarre asymmetric brachiopod, *Torquirhynchia inconstans* after which the bed is sometimes called the Inconstans Bed. This level is often best seen when exposed by cliff erosion at the western end of the low cliffs opposite the last holiday chalets (in the chalet called 'Faraways', Arkell wrote much of his *Memoir*). The top of the Corallian is taken at the underlying Ringstead Coral Bed (Bed 25) which has the colonial corals *Isastraea*, *Thamnasteria*, *Protoseris*, and the rare solitary coral *Montlivaltia* together with large, often spirally coiled, serpulid worm tubes of *Cycloserpula intestinalis*. The Ringstead Waxy Clays (3.2m) below are intermittently seen eastward towards Bran Point and include ferruginous micritic slabs and *Deltoideum*, *Ctenostreon* and serpulid tubes in abundance. The next locality may be reached by walking east by the cliff-top path from the car park.

13. HOLWORTH HOUSE AND WHITE NOTHE

This region may be approached either by foot from Ringstead, or by car from the field car park above South Down Farm (at SY 760823) and using the gated track past Falcon Barn: the car park is approached from the A353 by the road to Ringstead and continuing straight on at the hill top south of Upton. Narrow vehicles can approach direct from the A352 at Owermoigne (SY 767851) by using the narrow road and track which passes through the hamlet of Holworth. There is a field car park at the cliff top near Holworth House (SY 764816).

13A. Holworth House (SY 764814). Follow the track downhill from the car park to the cliffs just west of Holworth House. Here Portland and Purbeck Beds dipping 30° north are unconformably overlain by Gault with the overlying Upper Greensand dipping 12° southeast. The Portland and Purbeck Beds are themselves cut out (or displaced north) to the west by the Holworth House Fault which has a throw down to the east of about 45m. A map of the inferred pre-Albian geology is given in Fig. 4.

The succession of late Jurassic rocks seen at Holworth House is as follows:

PURBECK BEDS (Lulworth Beds) above

PORTLAND BEDS
Portland Freestone 6.4m
Cherty Series 10.4
Portland Sand 22.0

KIMMERIDGE CLAY
(On the downthrown side of the fault a sequence down to the White Stone Band 56m below the top can be traced ; the Blackstone is at shore level).

Townson (1975) noted that the Portland Freestone (his Winspit Member) already differs from the facies at Lulworth by the introduction of lime muds in the upper part rather than oolites: this facies change is further emphasised to the west.

13B. White Nothe (SY 772808). To examine the Cretaceous sequence of the Upper Greensand and Chalk south-east of Holworth House requires a traverse of the undercliff, and this is both time consuming and very rigorous. The Upper Greensand has a rich ammonite fauna of the Dispar Zone just below the the base of the Chalk and it can be worked at several places below the vertical cliffs west of White Nothe but provides precarious collecting. The basal Cenomanian is better examined in fallen blocks. The glauconitic Chalk Basement Bed is often crowded with the echinoid *Holaster*, with phosphatised and unphosphatised Middle Cenomanian ammonites and other fossils. The Lower Cenomanian appears to be missing.

The regional dip carries the base of the Chalk down to sea level at White Nothe itself and it can be reached on foot but with difficulty. The sequence of the Chalk can be examined with extreme difficulty in the cliffs towards White Nothe. From the top of the cliff near the Old Coastguard Station at White Nothe there is a convenient zig-zag path for the clear-headed which allows a descent (of 150m) to the shore. The traverse commences in the Coranguinum Zone of the Upper Chalk and most levels down to the Upper Greensand can be examined, but an intrepid, if not rash, spirit is needed. Wright (in Arkell 1947), Rowe (1901) and Mortimore and Pomerol (1987 p. 111) give details. If a boat is available to land on Lone Beach, between White Nothe and Bat's Head, an exceptionally complete

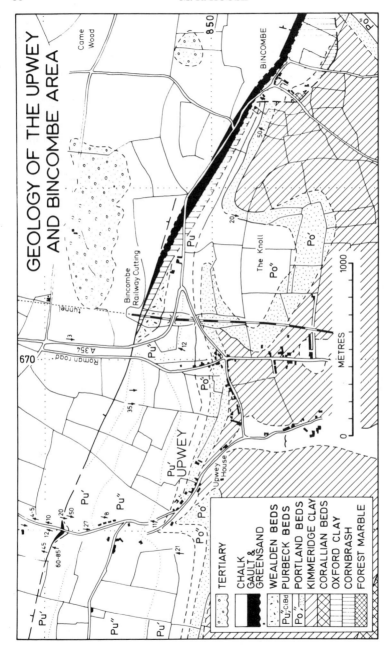

Figure 21.   Geological sketch map of the region around Upwey and the tectonic window
at Bincombe.

section of the Chalk can be examined which commences with striking microrhythmicity in the Cenomanian. At the east end of the Beach the Chalk dip steepens into the middle limb of the Purbeck Monocline (Plate 19C).

14. UPWEY TO SUTTON POYNTZ

The structures seen inland between near Upwey (SY 660860) and Chaldon Herring (791834), illustrated here by a series of maps and cross sections (Figs. 3, 4, 12, 21−29) show better than anywhere else at outcrop in Britain the interaction of pre-Albian and Tertiary structures.

The Ridgeway Fault forms a northern boundary and this fault has reactivated a pre-Albian fault downthrowing south which is named the Abbotsbury Fault. Erosion has excavated below the fault plane at Bincombe, and east and west of East Hill at Sutton Poyntz forming the well-known tectonic inliers. Also south of the Ridgeway Fault are the Tertiary anticlines of Sutton Poyntz, Poxwell and Chaldon and all of these were drilled in the early search for hydrocarbons. Some notes on the structures are given here from west to east.

14A. Gould's Bottom (SY 660860). The Ridgeway Fault passes north of the Friar Waddon Syncline 700m north west of Upwey (Fig. 21) and the fault trace crosses Gould's Bottom with the Purbeck Beds abutting Upper Chalk, but slivers of Upper Greensand and perhaps Portland Beds have been recognised against the fault plane (House 1961) witnessing to fault reactivation. On the east side of the road there are old quarries in both the Chalk and the Purbeck Beds. The Cinder Bed crops out in a roadside bluff 120m north of Upwey Church. At about 800m east of Upwey, in the ground between the Roman Road and the A354 there is a lower quarry in the Portland Beds above the road, and higher a fine quarry exposing 17.6m of the Lulworth Beds (at SY 671852).

14B. Bincombe Railway Cutting (SY 672853). This section is extremely interesting but exposures are variable and depend on small landslips. A sliver of Oxford Clay and lowest Corallian intervenes between Wealden Beds and Upper Chalk (House 1955) and traces of Upper Greensand and Gault have been found along the northern fault plane (Mottram 1950). The small landslips result from lubrication of the Oxford Clay by seep waters from the Chalk. The tectonic situation here can only be satisfactorily explained in terms of fault reactivation (Fig. 22). The cutting can be visited only with permission of British Rail.

14C. Bincombe (SY 686846). The Cornbrash in the tectonic inlier crops out in a farm drive west of the Church. The overlying Upper Greensand is well seen in a cutting to the north-west (SY 684847). Along the footpath which passes east from the village is a small quarry (SY 688845) which exposes the top of the Upper Greensand and the Lower Chalk. In the past the Chalk Basement Bed has been productive of ammonites here, especially *Calycoceras*, *Schloenbachia* and *Scaphites*. The underlying Upper Greensand has the bivalve *Merklina [Aequipecten] aspera*, the irregular echinoid *Cardiotaxis* and serpulid tubes. The next locality can be reached on foot by continuing east on the path. Otherwise

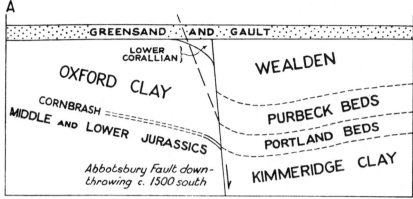

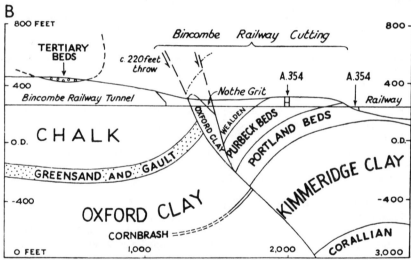

Figure 22.   Diagrams indicating the geology at the Bincombe railway cutting. Above, possible situation at the end of the Cretaceous and showing the effects of pre-Albian faulting and erosion. Below, present-day structure as a result of mid-Tertiary faulting and folding. The earlier, pre-Albian fault is usually called the Abbotsbury Fault and the later, Tertiary fault is called the Ridgeway Fault (modified from House 1958). For 1500′ read *ca.* 460m.

a detour by road has to be made via Broadwey and Littlemoor to the Combe Valley Road (Fig. 23).

14D. Green Hill and Chalbury (SY 696843). There is limited parking for a car near the farm buildings. The large scale accompanying map (Fig. 23) illustrates the newly revised interpretation here, the Survey maps being in error. Upper Greensand crops out along the wall 200m westnorthwest of Green Hill and

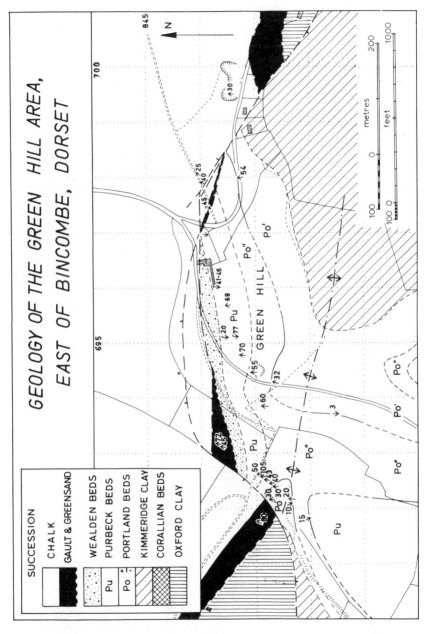

Figure 23.   Geological map of the area around Green Hill north-west of Sutton Poyntz.

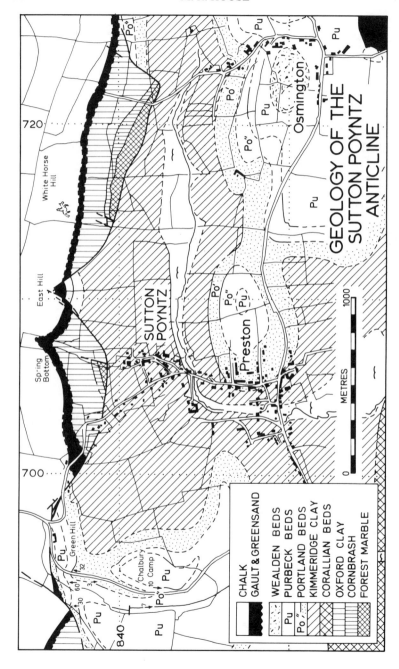

Figure 24. Geological sketch map of the Sutton Poyntz area showing the tectonic windows.

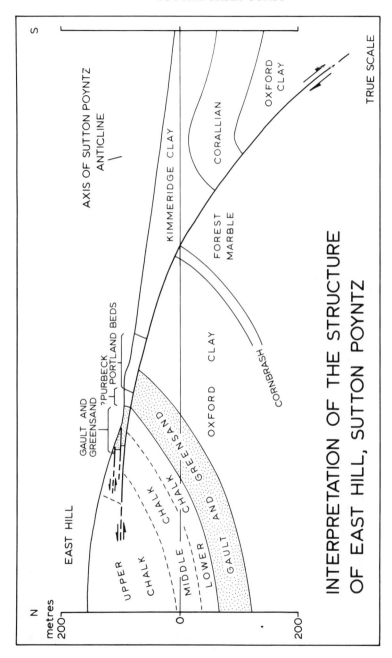

Figure 25. Geological cross section of the East Hill, Sutton Poyntz (modified from Arkell 1947).

is tectonically displaced from the outcrop followed by the path from Bincombe. The northern and western side of Green Hill shows a number of exposures of the Purbeck Beds and there is an old, small, quarry in the Portland Sand. The Cementstone forms a marked feature across the southern side of the Hill. On the west side of the road, in the core of the fold, are oyster beds with the small oyster *Nanogyra nana* (the Corton Hill Member of Townson 1975). Further south down the road in the Combe Valley and west of Chalbury (a hill fort) is a large quarry (SY 693837) in the Portland Limestone and Lower Purbeck Beds in which the Portland Stone level is represented by a softer, more marly limestone, typical of inland exposures further to the east. The Fossil Forest level and a basal Tufa of the Lower Purbeck Beds are well exposed. Return north along the road.

A silage pit on the west side of the road north and about 200m northwest of the farm buildings at Green Hill shows undisturbed Testudinarius Zone Upper Chalk. Yet 100m east of the buildings on the east side of the road to Sutton Poyntz, is a small quarry of Chalk, altered almost to a marble, which must abut the Ridgeway Fault. If the road is followed to the east towards Sutton Poyntz the oyster beds with *Nanogyra nana* are seen again in a cutting dipping north about 54°. Further east and down hill the Ridgeway Fault is again crossed. There is a large quarry on the north side of the road showing the nodular Middle Chalk and further down the road there is a fine cutting through the Upper Greensand near the beginning of the Sutton Poyntz tectonic inlier (Fig. 24).

14E. Sutton Poyntz (SY 706837). It is possible to park small vehicles in Sutton Poyntz close to the Spring Head Hotel near the duck pond. Trenches dug on the west side of the pond, outside cottages numbered 103–109, have provided a fauna of the Lower Kimmeridge Clay *Aulacostephanus* zones indicating proximity to the axis of the Sutton Poyntz anticline. A track west of the water-works leads from the duck pond to a path through two fields to a small stream from Spring Bottom (Fig. 24). Immediately south of the second gate the path crosses, and where the stream takes a bend, is a former prospect pit in the Kimmeridge Clay at the level of the Blackstone (Kimmeridge Oil Shale). Continuing through the gate, and only a few metres to the north, Forest Marble is exposed in the stream and the beds are near-vertical or overturned. The Abbotsbury or pre-Albian Fault intervenes between the Kimmeridge Clay and the Forest Marble (Fig. 25). When the adjacent field is under plough abundant fossil evidence for the Lower Cornbrash is readily obtainable, but the former Cornbrash outcrop in the stream appears to have been cemented over.

The path continues to join a path at the foot of the Downs, and if this is followed to the slight knoll (at SY 704843) the grits of the Upper Greensand can be seen projecting through the turf around the knoll. By retracing and walking above the water reservoir at the spring head around the railings it is possible to reach East Hill, the next locality, but this is not a right of way.

14F. East Hill (SY 709843). A track just north of the Spring Head Hotel leads east from the duck pond to a field gate whence the path goes up to East Hill. The route is wholly on Kimmeridge Clay and an auger will prove the typical steel-blue colours which distinguish it from the soft khaki-orange colours of the Oxford Clay. At an old fence boundary about half way up the field, preserved usually now as a low electric fence corner, remnants of a former outcrop of one of the Upper Kimmeridge Clay stone bands can be traced. Later the path enters a small cutting in the Portland Beds and Gault and Upper Greensand, but only the uppermost part of the latter is exposed. On the west side of the cutting, at the junction with the Chalk, pockets of Lower Cenomanian fossils are, unusually, preserved in the Chalk Basement Bed (Hancock 1963). On the east side, the boundary is seen to be thrust north, and the Upper Greensand grits can be traced eastward, and then are cut again by a thrust to reappear beyond the wall and some 60m to the northeast on the slopes of the down (Figs. 24, 25).

15. POXWELL AND CHALDON HERRING

In this area, reached by following the A353 east from Weymouth, the structures seen in the tectonic windows at Bincombe and Sutton Poyntz are well beneath the surface. But early attempts to search for oil in the 'pop-up' folds of the Poxwell and Chaldon periclines led to the documentation of the relationships at depth.

15A. Poxwell (SY 742842). There is limited parking by the bend in the road south of Poxwell (at SY 742835). Along the northern side of the Poxwell Pericline (Fig. 26) Gault and Upper Greensand are now known to be more extensive than shown on current Survey maps (Mottram 1950, Mottram and House 1956). The Poxwell borehole (see Arkell 1947) was drilled (at SY 748835) by d'Arcy Exploration Co. in 1937 (Fig. 27). The Poxwell Bend Quarry (SY 744835) exposes Portland Freestone and lower Purbeck Beds, the former with lime mudstones above rhaxellid wackestones and cherts. At the base of the Purbeck Beds is a 0.3m basal cast bed with small gastropods, bivalves, ostracods and sponge spicules (Clements 1967).

There is a very fine overview of the Poxwell Pericline from above the quarry. This has been described as "perhaps the finest small-scale pericline in the country" (Sylvester-Bradley 1948, with an aerial photograph on pl.13).

The rather overgrown road cutting (SY 742834) west of the road bend still exposes the Cinder Bed and associated units of the Purbeck Beds described by Sylvester-Bradley (1949) but a scrabble in undergrowth is required to examine it. The Cinder Bed (0.5m thick) is full of the oyster *Praeexogyra distorta* and the Cypridea Bed (10cm thick and 4.4m below the Cinder Bed) is largely composed of the small ostracod *Cypridea granulosa*. Old quarries in the Lulworth Formation about 200m north-west of the road bend (at about SY 739835) yield insect remains in white chalky micrites.

15B. Five Marys (SY 788842). Travelling to or from Lulworth a narrow road can be followed which leaves the A352 2km east of Owermoigne and goes south to East Chaldon (and on to Winfrith Newburgh and Lulworth). Near the crest of the hill is a vantage point on the road giving an overview of the site of the

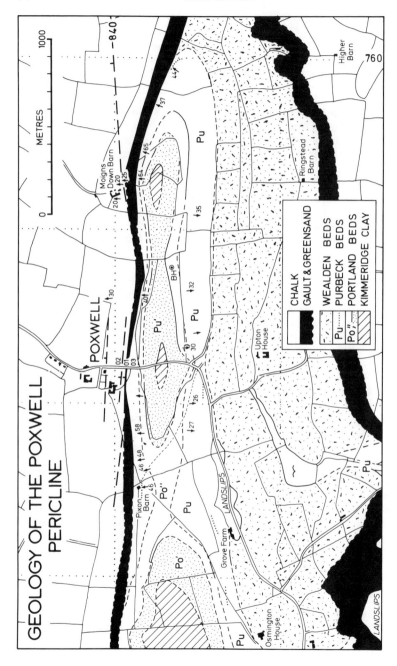

Figure 26.   Geological sketch map of the Poxwell Anticline.

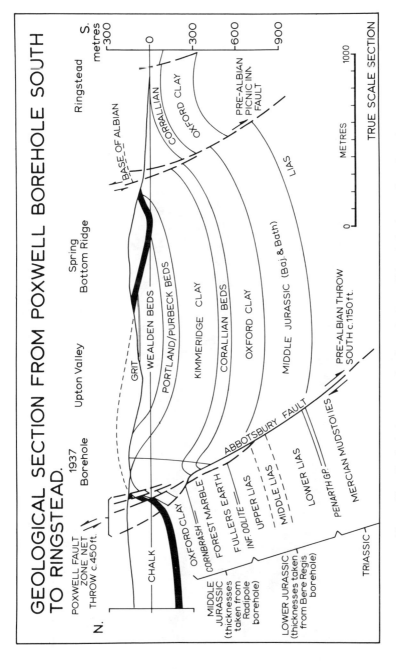

Figure 27.   Geological cross section from the Poxwell borehole site southwards to the coast (modified from Mottram and House 1956).

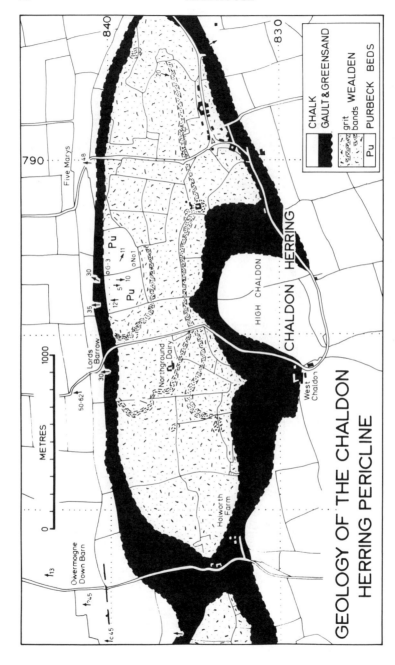

GEOLOGY OF THE CHALDON
HERRING PERICLINE

Figure 28.   Geological sketch map of the Chaldon Herring are with course of grit bands
in the Wealden taken from A. H. Taitt (in Arkell 1947).

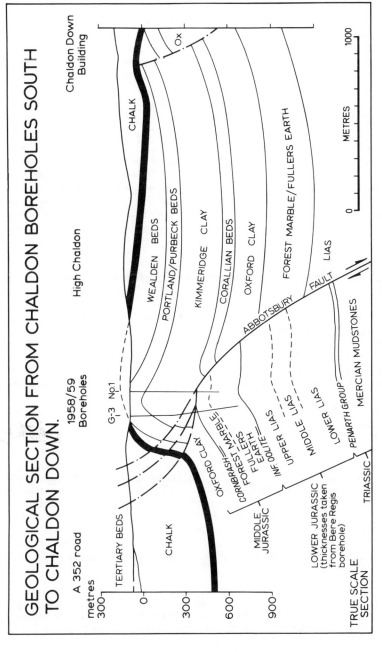

Figure 29. Geological cross section from the Chaldon boreholes south to the coast (modified from House 1961).

British Petroleum wells of 1954 and 1955 (Figs. 28, 29). Details of the wells were published by House (1961) with an interpretation as indicated on an accompanying diagram. Ridd (1973) has offered an interpretation dependent on a near horizontal thrust in the Kimmeridge Clay and no reactivation of the pre-Albian fault but there is no evidence of such structure where the Abbotsbury Fault is exposed at surface near Sutton Poyntz and the fault plane is also very flat-lying.

It would seem likely that the Pre-Albian fault, which has maintained its powerful throw for the fifteen miles (24 km) from Abbotsbury to this point may, without Tertiary reactivation, be part of the same fault belt which links directly or *en echelon* with the main southern fault of the Wytch Farm field (Fig. 40). If this were so, Oxford Clay would be the unit on which Gault was deposited on the north side of the Abbotsbury Fault all the way from Wytch Farm to Portesham. The northern pre-Albian fault, with a northern downthrow, at Wytch Farm (Fig. 40) is suggested by Chadwick (1986) to pass east to the Bridport area to the Bothenhampton/Shipton Gorge Fault (but there the down-throw is to the south).

16. MORETON

Inland areas are best for seeing the terrace gravels of the Frome valley. General aspects of the geology relating to these were given in the Introduction.

16A. Warmwell and Moreton (SY 753864, 779891). There are several large quarries in the sands and gravels of the Bagshot Beds facies (Bournemouth Group) near Warmwell (SY 753864) and near Moreton Railway Station (SY. 779891) (ECC Quarries Ltd, Warmwell, Tel. 0305 852256). Pleistocene flint gravels of the Moreton terrace can be seen to 6.5m at Owermoigne Heath Pit (SY 779880), one kilometre south of the station. At 1.3km southeast of the station is Pearson's Pit (SY 789882), near Red Bridge, which shows the Moreton Terrace on sands of the Bagshot Beds. The terrace hereabouts is mostly a gravel of subangular flints, Upper Greensand cherts and vein quartz, but it has also provided 'Chellian' and Acheulian flint implements (some figured in Arkell, 1947).

16B. Culpepper's Dish (SY 814926). This is 5km northeast of Moreton station and is a spectacular sinkhole or doline. Some 50,000 cubic metres of sediment must have disappeared into a solution cavern below. It is the largest of many such structures developed in a belt here where the Tertiary Beds thin to a feather edge on the northern side of the Frome Syncline. The evidence at Studland (see below) and elsewhere shows that there are many solution holes along the junction of the Chalk and the Tertiaries. A review of the Dorset sinkholes is given by Sperling *et al.* (1977).

Clouds Hill (SY 824909), 1.8km southeast of the previous locality is the fascinating cottage of Lawrence of Arabia (1888–1935) whose splendid effigy, in arab dress, and carved withal of Portland Stone, is in the Saxon St Martin's Church, Wareham (SY 922877): this may be surprising place to find it but he is said to have helped the restoration of the church; it is also said the effigy was originally intended for Salisbury Cathedral. His less impressive grave is in Moreton Cemetery (SY 803893).

17. DURDLE DOOR, LULWORTH COVE AND MUPE BAY

The Lulworth coast has been dissected by marine erosion so that it displays the detailed relations of the Upper Jurassic and Cretaceous rocks of the middle limb of the Purbeck Monocline (Figs. 1a, 31, 32). The Upper Chalk at the coast is mostly vertical or overturned. The main dip sections through the structure are seen at Durdle Cove, Man-o'-War Cove, St Oswald's Bay and on the west and east sides of Lulworth Cove. It is a famous area for showing the stages of marine erosion (Fig. 30). The foresyncline of the Purbeck Monocline passes out to sea west of Bat's Head (Plate 19C; this shows that there is no fault along this line as wrongly shown by Brunsden and Goudie 1981, p. 32).

The Lulworth Borehole (Fig. 30) gave the following section through the Cretaceous having started close to the base of the Tertiary Beds:

Upper Chalk .... c. 305.0m
Middle Chalk 57.9
Lower Chalk 45.7
Upper Greensand and Gault 53.5
  (Kimmeridge Clay below)

There is a general thinning of units in the Lulworth area, minimum figures being in the Durdle Door to Dungy Head region. Lower Greensand has been recorded as 0.3m thick in Lulworth Cove. It is overstepped westward but it thickens eastward to 25m in Worbarrow Bay and 61m at Swanage. Along the Lulworth coast Wealden Beds are still preserved but a pre-Albian fault beneath the line of the foresyncline brings Jurassic rocks beneath the unconformity as indicated by the Lulworth borehole (Fig. 31) and at White Nothe. The Jurassic rocks too, thin in the Lulworth area where the Portland and Purbeck Beds are about 40m and 54m thickening to 64m and 88m respectively by Worbarrow Bay. The thinning of units has been ascribed to a northwest to southeast trending 'Mid-Dorset Swell' (Drummond 1970), but a sedimentary thinning related to east-west trending growth faults, and in this case a pre-Albian fault line, seems more likely.

The middle limb of the monocline is vertical or overturned but to the south older units dip at progressively lesser amounts to the north. The axial trace of the foresyncline runs east-west rather inland of the coast but it passes out to sea west of Bat's Head (Plate 19C).

In the late Jurassic rocks there are two noteworthy types of structure:

1.   The *Lulworth Crumple* affects the Purbeck Beds especially at Stair Hole (Plate 20A): these small folds and faults are interpreted by Phillips (1964) as gravity collapse structures.

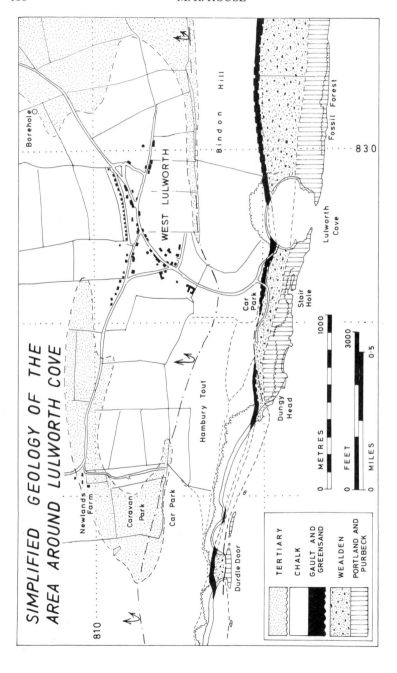

Figure 30.   Geological sketch map of the Lulworth district.

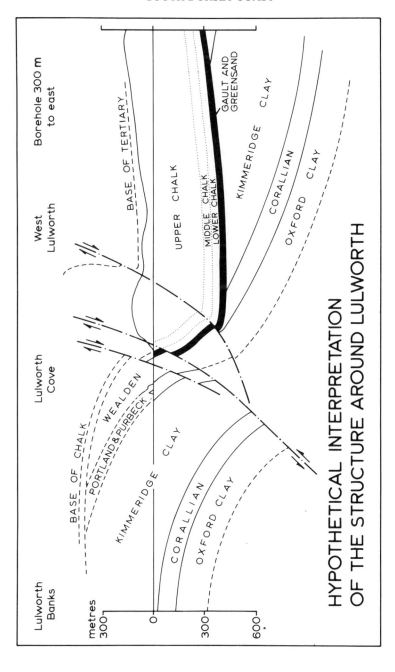

Figure 31. Geological cross section north-south through Lulworth Cove and showing the relationship to the Lulworth borehole.

2. The *Lulworth Broken Beds* comprise an interval of brecciated limestones
    set within normally bedded early Purbeck Beds. These have been variously
    interpreted as either:
    (a) Penecontemporaneous structures caused by collapse of overlying beds
         following either solution of evaporites or decay of vegetation, or,
    (b) Penecontemporaneous brecciation resulting from contemporary
         faulting associated with a pre-Mid-Cretaceous growth fault along the
         axis of the foresyncline of the Purbeck Fold, or,
    (c) Brecciation resulting from tectonic accommodation of the rather
         incompetent Purbeck beds in relation to the more competent Portland
         beds and Chalk during the main mid-Tertiary folding.
    (d) Tectonic evaporation breccias in which tectonically fragmented blocks
         and early calcitised evaporites set in an evaporite matrix were later
         calcitised (West 1975, West *et al.*, 1969).

Within the Chalk is a series of shears and faults which may conveniently be
categorised using Arkell's notation in the *Memoir*. The genetic interpretation was
revised by Phillips (1964). Bevan (1985) has shown that much simplification
results if the fractures are related to bedding, in which case conjugate pairs are
recognisable which have been rotated by subsequent folding. Arkell's notation as
now revised is as follows:

GROUP 1.   Shear planes dipping 60°–70° south, coinciding with overturned
            bedding and formed by bedding or flexural slip during folding.
GROUP 2.   Shear planes dipping 50°–70° north, formed primarily as a result
            of tension.
GROUP 3.   Shears typically dipping 25°–40° south but some pass into thrusts
            dipping 0–20° south. Argued by Bevan (1985) to be conjugate with
            Group 2 shears when considered in relation to bedding planes and
            resulting from extension during folding.
GROUP 4.   Steep reverse faults with dips of 70°–40° south. Downthrowing
            north and often with thick crush breccias.
GROUP 5.   Reverse faults overthrust to the south with dips of 35°–55° north.
GROUP 6.   Reverse faults dipping 35° north.

17A. Durdle Cove (SY 805803). The most convenient access to Durdle Door,
Durdle Cove and Man-o'-War Cove is reached from a car park (SY 812804) near
Newlands Farm beyond a caravan park. This is approached by a turn at the crest
of the hill west from Lulworth. From the car park there are paths to the cliff top
at Durdle Door to the west (Fig. 30). For St Oswalds Bay, Dungy Head and
Lulworth Cove easiest access is from the car park at Lulworth Cove (SY 822801).
Mid or low tides are needed to pass Man-o'-War Head at beach level.

West of Durdle Door, Bat's Head shows vertical Upper Chalk (the tip is in the
Planus Zone, the lower cliff is in the Cortestudinarium Zone and the back cliff
Coranguinum Zone), the Chalk being cut by Group 3 shears (Figure 32). Swyre
Head is of vertical Coranguinum Zone cut by Group 3 shears which pass into
low thrusts now eroded as caves at the foot of the cliff. In Durdle Cove, north
of the Door, the Cenomanian Basement Bed at the base of the Chalk is well

exposed and the Basement Bed is fossiliferous with glauconitic marl and phosphatic nodules above. Higher the Plenus Marl is well seen. To the south is a prominent wall of Upper Greensand dipping 77° south with chert nodules especially in the upper part associated with *Thalassinoides* burrows. The Gault basal pebble bed, with pea-sized, rounded clasts, can often be traced cutting down onto lower levels of the Wealden in its course from the lower to upper cliff giving a pre-Gault dip of about 10° north and indicating a pre-Albian roll-over structure. At the 'neck' of the Durdle promontory the lower Wealden and upper Purbeck Beds are cut out by a strike fault but the Cinder Bed is seen.

17B. Man-o'-War Cove (SY 807802) (Plate 19B). If a descent is made on the east side of Durdle Door good sections of the Broken Beds and of lower Purbeck Beds (Lulworth Beds) up to the Cinder Bed (Table VII) can be examined. The upper Purbeck and lower Wealden Beds are cut out by the same strike fault as on the west side of the promontory. To the north a thick Quartz Grit, with Armorican pebbles, is seen in the middle of the purple, red and yellow sands and silts of the Wealden Beds and the sequence can be followed up to the Upper Greensand. It is often badly slipped but occasionally the basal pebble bed of the Gault can be traced. The junction with the Lower Chalk is shown in the western side of the Cove and also, at low tide, below Man-o'-War Head: the main cliff there shows overturned Upper Chalk with Group 1 and 2 shears well developed, separated by a Group 4 fault from northward dipping nodular Middle Chalk to the south. The Upper Greensand/Chalk boundary can be traced on foreshore reefs as can the Plenus Marl. At high spring tides it is not possible to round Man-o'-War Point.

17C. St Oswald's Bay (SY 810803). The east side of Man-o'-War Head shows Middle Chalk, approximately vertical, cut by Group 3 shears, and then the Group 4 fault previously seen, here dipping 40° south, introduces overturned Upper Chalk of the Cortestudinarium and Coranguinum Zones cut into blocks by Group 1 and 2 shears. A prominent solution pipe cuts vertically through the Chalk almost to beach level and a lignitic horizon in the filling gravels has yielded recent pollen; this solution hole must post-date the folding (House 1965, p.39). To the east a Group 5 fault (dip 55° north) brings Middle Chalk against Plenus Marls and Lower Chalk. Then follows a sequence of Upper Greensand and Gault.

17D. Dungy Head (SY 815800). Just above beach level, where the footpath to Lulworth Cove climbs up from St Oswald's Cove, there are oil seeps out of the Wealden. To the south the Purbeck and Portland Beds are exposed but the former is reduced in thickness by faulting. The Portland Beds section at Dungy Head is particularly good and shows the Portland Sand well. Here the terminology of Townson (1975) is given in parenthesis since it has not been widely followed (Cope *et al.*, 1980).

PORTLAND FREESTONE
    Oolites above with medium to coarse bioclast sand below
      (Winspit Member) 11.5m

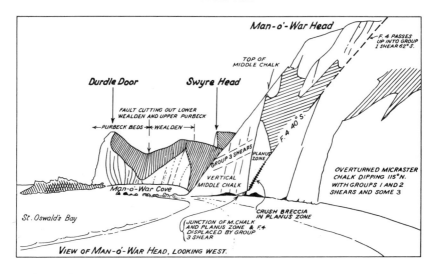

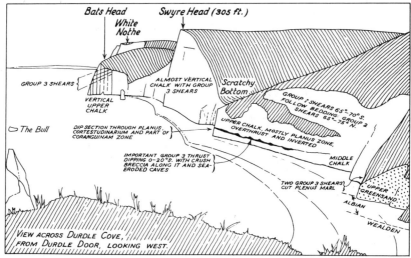

Figure 32.   The Dorset coast between Man-o'-War Head and Bat's Head showing features of geological interest (from House 1958).

CHERTY SERIES

Shelly bioclastic limestones (Dancing Ledge Member) 5.0

Rhaxella wackestone with a soft easily weathered chert-free bed (Bed J of Arkell, 0.58m) at the top full of bivalves and *Thalassinoides* (Dungy Head Member) 5.6

PORTLAND SAND

Fine grained dolomites with The Black Sandstones (4.1m) at
the top and the Cast Bed with abundant bivalves at the
base (1.4m) (Gad Cliff Member) 6.1

The Exogyra Beds full of *Nanogyra nana* and *Glomerula*
(Corton Hill Member) 1.2m

Black dolomitic siltstones and shales (Black Nore Member) .   21.3

The route by the footpath to Lulworth Cove shows progressive convergence
of the Chalk and Purbeck Beds ridges due to the effect of a significant strike fault.

17E.   Lulworth Cove (SY 825799). There is an enormous car park close to the
Cove. Access to the Fossil Forest and further east will depend on whether the
army gunnery ranges are open: they usually are on Sundays and Bank Holidays
and for much of August. The Commandant, Lulworth Firing Range, Lulworth
Camp will give information (Tel. (0929) 462721 Ext.819 or The Guardroom,
Ext.824). Walk up the slight hill to the west side of the Cove overlooking Stair
Hole and the Cove. The Portland Beds form the horns at the mouth of the Cove
and the bay itself is eroded from the softer beds of the Wealden. The fine Chalk
cliffs of Bindon Hill form the backdrop (Plate 21A).

On the west side, the sections at Stair Hole provide a full sequence of the
Purbeck Beds (53.6m) with the Cinder Bed separating the Lulworth Beds (below)
from the Durlston Beds (above) (Plate 20A,B). The contorted beds in the upper
cliff are referred to as the Lulworth Crumple. The early stages of a coastal erosion
sequence are shown here by breaching tunnels through the Portland Stone; later
the softer Purbeck and Wealden Beds were eroded out. Next, as illustrated in the
western end, collapse produces an opening which later erosion will extend. In this
way longer-term erosion produces structures of the size of Lulworth Cove and
Worbarrow Bay. However, erosion at Lulworth and Worbarrow was probably
developed along preexisting valleys during the Flandrian transgression so this is
not a simple reflection of local coastal development.

The upper cliff behind Lulworth Cove, cut into Bindon Hill, comprises
overturned Upper Chalk of the Cortestudinarium and Coranguinum Zones. A
marked Group 4 fault separates the overturned Upper Chalk from the Middle and
Lower Chalk of the lower cliff which dips about $55° - 65°$ north. The Gault and
Upper Greensand strike across the head of the Cove from the outlet and an old
lime kiln (Plate 21B), past Black Rocks to the eastern side where Lower
Greensand (0.3m) has been reported.

The most instructive section commences at the stream outlet by the café and
follows the coast to the east along the cliffs to Mupe Bay beyond the Fossil Forest
but much time is needed for that. To approach the exposures on the east side the
obvious route is along the beach, but that route can be followed on the return.
The fine views provided by the footpath which goes up beside the café to the high
cliff of Bindon Hill should be enjoyed on the outward walk. The footpath drops
on the east side of Bindon Hill and can give access to the beach where the Upper
Greensand, Gault, Lower Greensand and Wealden Beds sequence is intermittently exposed in the badly slipped cliffs. This is the westernmost point where

the Lower Greensand is seen and it is a 0.3 m ironstone with the bivalves *Exogyra*, *Eomiodon* and *Filosina* (Casey 1961).

Towards the eastern horn area of Lulworth Cove there are excellent outcrops of the Purbeck Beds. For details the log in the *Memoir* (Arkell 1947) is required. The Cinder Bed and Cherty Freshwater Bed below it are well seen close to where the rock promontory begins, and the exposures of the Broken Beds near the horn in Potter's Hole are quite spectacular. Here the basal Lulworth Formation shows beds with replaced evaporites, algal mats, stromatolites and dirt beds. Nevertheless this is an extremely dangerous place, especially after winter rains; several members of a geological party were killed in February 1977 by a rock fall of Purbeck Beds from higher in the cliff. The advice is to avoid these exposures since similar horizons are seen at the next locality.

17F. Fossil Forest (SY 829797)(Plate 28). The right of way does not descend to Potter's Hole but continues to the cliff top. The Ministry of Defence have built a stairway to the undercliff near the firing range flagpost for descent to the Fossil Forest (Fig. 30). Here there is a northward dipping ledge of earliest Purbeckian with fine exposures of the Broken Beds associated with northward overfolding and also the famous Fossil Forest (Francis 1983) (Plate 22).

The Portland Stone, which forms the seaward cliffs, dips north and is overlain by the Purbeck Beds at the base of which is the Hard Cap (4.7m) of laminated limestones with oolites and limestones with pseudomorphs after gypsum. On top of this is the Great Dirt Bed, at the same level as on Portland and into which the trees of the Fossil Forest were rooted. This forms a series of boles of trees and fallen trunks enclosed in algal tufa (Pugh 1968). Little trace of the actual woody tissue has been preserved but it is now represented by hollows. The tree boles are engulfed by the Soft Cap (1.5m) of stromatolitic limestone. These often show evidence of replacement of anhydrite and also pseudomorphs after gypsum, and reticulate structures indicating replacement of gypsum. These relationships were established by West (1975, 1979, West *et al.*, 1969). In particular West has demonstrated a sequence of stages by which primary gypsum may pass from lenticular then anhedral crystals to anhydrite, and by hydration to a range of secondary gypsum fabrics or, by calcite replacement, to limestones and by silicification to cherts with pseudomorphs after anhydrite. Andrews (1988) has described the associated microfabrics, especially in relation to the calcrete palaeosol levels. The brecciated limestones of the Broken Beds follow and are of variable thickness (about 5m). The association of the Broken Beds with evaporites, demonstrated by West, suggests a more complex history than simple collapse and brecciation following dissolution of evaporites (Hollingworth, 1938). West prefers a solution involving tectonically brecciated blocks of limestone and early calcitised evaporites set in an evaporite matrix which was later calcitised (West, 1975, 1979; West *et al.*, 1969).

The 'Cypris' Freestone is a laminated ostracod limestone about 5.5m thick. At a level of about one metre above, in the Soft Cockle Beds, is a 3–14cm pellet limestone which has halite pseudomorphs on both the upper and lower surfaces, really only explicable by dissolution of the salt before cementation of the pellets (House 1966). There are other fascinating lithologies, ripple marked surfaces, mud-cracked surfaces, ostracod limestones and beds full of the bivalve *Neomiodon* or gastropods, or enigmatic structures, perhaps trace fossils, or perhaps due to desiccation, and most posing problems of origin and interpretation.

17G. Mupe Bay (SY 843797). If the firing range is open the cliff-top footpath can be followed to above Bacon Hole where the profile of the eastern side of Worbarrow Bay can be seen in the distance (Fig. 18b). Bacon Hole itself has a fine section through the Purbeck Beds, including the Broken Beds at the base and the whole of the Lulworth and Durlston Formations. In Mupe Bay the northward dip gives outcrops of the Wealden Beds. At 24m above the base, and seen just to the north of where the steps lead down to Mupe Bay, is a channel sand impregnated with oil, one of the several local oil seeps which encouraged oil exploration before the Second World War. This seep gave rise to views that it was contemporary with Wealden sedimentation but these are now discounted (Miles *et al.*, 1993). Higher horizons up to the Upper Chalk (Mortimore and Pomerol 1987, p. 111) can be examined on the north side of Mupe Bay if this is permitted. For a return to Lulworth there are two footpaths. One follows the hollow of the Wealden Beds due west back to Lulworth Cove and the beach walk to the road. The other path leads due north to the top of Bindon Hill and can give exceptionally fine views of coastline eastwards to St Alban's Head: there is then a path from the top to the western end of Bindon Hill which drops down to the café at Lulworth Cove.

EAST DORSET COAST

The most convenient coastal road from Lulworth to the east is via Whiteway Hill and through the firing ranges, but this is frequently closed except for most weekends and Bank Holidays. Advice is given on a signpost in East Lulworth or The Commandant, Lulworth Firing Ranges can advise (telephone numbers given earlier). Otherwise the approach to the following itineraries is via Wareham (Fig. 38). Because of narrow roads, coaches can only travel in the Isle of Purbeck area with permission of The County Surveyor, County Hall, Dorchester (Tel. 0305 251975). Thus the factors of heathland and the marshes along the Frome valley, which isolated the Isle of Purbeck in the Dark Ages and in Mediaeval times, and gave it the name, have been replaced by yet other inconveniences today. So whilst St Alban's Head might seem the natural boundary between South and East Dorset, in practice the boundary is at Worbarrow Bay, and that is adopted here.

If Wool is on the route, Woolbridge Manor (SY 844873) is a fine Dorset manor house started in the 17th century. It is the fictional ancestral home of Hardy's Tess of the D'Urbervilles and was the real home of the Turbeville family. The house has some of the best early Dorset brick work and is partly roofed with Purbeck flags. The nearby ancient bridge over the Frome has parapets of Portland Stone and ferruginous gritstone. A notice dating from George the Fourth threatens anyone damaging the bridge with transportation for life.

	DURDLE DOOR	WORBARROW TOUT	DURLSTON BAY
DURLSTON FORMATION			
Upper 'Cypris' Clays and Shales		5.3	11.4 + m
Unio Beds	Higher Beds Faulted Out	0.6	1.1
Broken Shell Lst			2.8
Chief Beef Beds		7.3	8.0
Corbula Beds		5.3	10.2
Scallop Beds		1.9	1.5
Intermarine Beds		6.8	15.2
Cinder Bed	0.9	2.1	2.8
LULWORTH FORMATION			
Cherty Freshwater Beds	1.1	7.6	8.1
Marly Freshwater Beds		4.3	3.9
Soft Cockle Beds	11.5	15.0	24.8
Hard Cockle Beds			3.7
'Cypris' Freestones	5.3	14.7	13.7
Broken Beds and Caps	6.0	6.6	8.5

TABLE VII. Table giving the thicknesses of units of the Purbeck Beds between Durdle Door and Durlston Bay. Data from Arkell (1947), Ensom (1985a), Clements (1969), Melville and Freshney (1982) and Cosgrove and Hearn (1966).

Probably the finest cliff-top walk in Dorset is the route from the car park at the top of Whiteway Hill (SY 888811) via the footpath 3km west to the Iron Age fort of Flower's Barrow (SY 863805) (Fig. 18c) and then down the cliff-top path to Worbarrow Tout. By continuing on the coastal footpath up along the precipice at the top of Gad Cliff a descent can be made by a cliff-top path above Brandy Bay to Broad Bench, Gaulter Gap, and the car park at Kimmeridge (with welcome refreshment at the Post Office or on to the next itinerary).

18. WORBARROW BAY

This splendid bay, with its continuous sequence from the Portland Beds to the Upper Chalk, can be approached when the Ministry of Defence allows via the now deserted village of Tyneham where there is a car park (SY 882802) and a 1.4km walk by a track to the shore. Access is possible for rather longer periods during August holiday times but otherwise mostly on Sundays and Bank Holidays only (Plate 23).

18A. Worbarrow Tout (SY 869796). The promontory of Worbarrow Tout, at the southern end of the Bay, exposes a fine section of the limestones of the Purbeck Beds, described in detail by Ensom (1985a). The succession and thicknesses are shown in Table VII. This section is best studied after examination of the Durlston sequence where fuller details of the units are given (Itinerary 22A).

18B. Worbarrow Bay (SY 867802). The multicoloured Wealden Beds of red, yellow and purple clays and sands are 425m thick (Arkell 1947) with the Quartz Grit (6.0m) almost exactly in the middle. The Lower Greensand is 25m thick and comprises grey and black sandstones with ironstone levels and horizons of marginal-marine bivalves. The Punfield Marine Bed (see Itinerary 23B) is here a fossiliferous ironstone with the bivalves *Eomiodon* and *Cuneocorbula* (Casey 1961) and the gastropod *Cassiope*. The Gault has a 0.3m quartz and lydite pebble bed at the base and comprises black and glauconitic siltstones and sandstones which pass up into more massive sandstones of the Upper Greensand giving a total thickness of 57m for the Albian stage. The ammonites *Hoplites*, *Callihoplites*, *Anahoplites*, *Durnovarites* and *Stoliczkaia* have been recorded (Wright *in* Arkell 1947). The Cenomanian Basement Bed, at the base of the Chalk, has yielded a good ammonite fauna including *Calycoceras*, *Mantelliceras* and *Scaphites*. Higher levels to the Middle Chalk have been accessible at Cow Corner (Fig. 18) but recent landslips may have obscured part of the section (Mortimore and Pomerol 1987, p. 111). Higher levels of the Chalk in Mupe Bay and at Arish Mell were described by Rowe (1901) (Plate 23B).

19. KIMMERIDGE BAY TO FRESHWATER STEPS

Kimmeridge Bay (Fig. 33) has a cliff-top car park which is reached from Kimmeridge village by a toll road. The continuous cliff section around Kimmeridge Bay (SY 907790) and eastward to Chapman's Pool (SY 957770) forms the type section for the mid and late Kimmeridgian Stage nationally. There is usually a Warden here in summer and hammering is not allowed except with the permission of the Smedmore Estate, Smedmore House, Kimmeridge.

Clavell's Hard is a half-hour walk from the car park. To proceed further needs very much longer time. A rope may be needed for a descent at Clavell's Hard and, in recent times, the occasional collapse of the ladder at Freshwater Steps has meant that it is not possible to climb up there. Hence it is not advisable to go beyond the undercliff adit at Clavell's Hard unless sound preparations have been made and the exact tidal situation known.

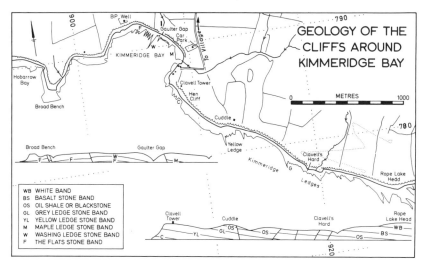

Figure 33.   Sketch map of the geology around Kimmeridge showing the main cement-
stones seen in the cliffs.

The lowest Kimmeridge Clay here is not seen at outcrop (erosion not having cut so deeply into core of the Purbeck Anticline along the coast), but it was proved to a depth of 243m in the B.P. well near Gaulter Gap. The accompanying rock succession (Table VIII) gives the sequence up to the Portland Beds around Chapman's Pool. The actual sequence readily seen by short walks from the car park at Kimmeridge (SY 909791) is indicated on the map and corresponding cliff profiles (Figs. 18d, 33). The east-west axis of the Purbeck Anticline passes through Kimmeridge Bay.

Aulacostephanid ammonites (ribbed and with a smooth central band on the venter) go up to the unnamed cementstone below Clavell Tower (marked 'C' on Fig. 33) and their upper limit marks the top of the Lower Kimmeridgian (or the *whole* of the Kimmeridgian of near-universal continental usage). The crushed giant ammonite *Gravesia* then occurs in shales up to the Yellow Stone Band. The entry of this new fauna is usually taken to define the base of the Volgian of the Boreal Realm and the base of the Tithonian of Mediterranean usage.

Most obvious in the cliffs is the pattern of rhythmic or cyclic deposition on the scale of a metre or so. In the section of Kimmeridge Clay exposed here Downie (1955) has identified 141 cycles. The pattern is as follows (Downie *in* House 1969, Tyson *et al.*, 1979, Cox and Gallois 1981):

D.   COCCOLITH LIMESTONES. Either with fine original laminations of dark sapropel-rich levels and light coccolith layers or the same homo-genised by bioturbation (Plates 16–18).

C.   OIL SHALE. Shale with up to 70% organic matter. The best developed level has been variously called the Blackstone, the Oil Shale, and Kimmeridge Coal (Plate 15).

B.   BITUMINOUS SHALE. Clays or shales as in A below but with organic matter up to 30%.

A.   CLAYS. Shales and clays predominantly of illite with up to 10% organic matter.

The pattern of repetition of these units varies from a rhythmic (or asymmetric cyclic) ABAB or ABCABC pattern to cyclic (or symmetric cyclic) ABCBA, ABDBA, or ABCDCBA pattern. The coccolith limestones (Plate 16) reach their maximum development above the Lower Kimmeridge Clay and die out in the late Upper Kimmeridge Clay. Approximately in the middle of this development is the Blackstone or Kimmeridge Oil Shale. Many of the limestone levels are now dolomites and weather orange-yellow: these now show no evidence of coccoliths under the stereoscan electron microscope.

Interpretations of the rhythm and cycle facies falls conveniently into two classes. Gallois (1976) has argued that surface or near surface algal blooms, including coccolith and dinoflagellate blooms, could so deoxygenate and poison waters that bottom conditions would be produced favouring the preservation of organic material: this interpretation puts the main control as the surface distribution of algae and its rhythmic or cyclic changes. On the other hand, Tyson, Wilson and Downie (1979) have argued that the cycles are best interpreted in terms of vertical migrations and oscillations of the $O:H_2S$ interface near the sea floor, a view compatible with current interpretations of the Black Sea and Nile Cone sea floor sediments. Perhaps particularly relevant is their argument that modern precipitation of high Mg-calcites in the Mediterranean is inversely related to water-mass stratification; they point out that dolomites tend to be more common in the Kimmeridge succession where oil shales and coccolith limestones are well developed. The importance of climatic change has been stressed by Wignall and Ruffell (1990).

Fluctuations of the $O:H_2S$ level must be used with caution since there is a modest occurrence of benthic bivalves, particularly ostreids and lucinoids together with lingulid brachiopods which were benthonic and could not have survived total anoxia during their growth. Where the Kimmeridge Clay thins, as westward towards Osmington Mills, there is a progressive reduction in the number of limestones and dolomites. By Sutton Poyntz and towards Abbotsbury only the White Stone Band has been recognised and this might suggest that deeper water conditions lay towards the east and that there are changes in rhythmic or cyclic pattern related to depth thresholds. Oschmann (1988) has suggested cyclic spreads of anoxia over the continental shelf on which the Kimmeridge Clay was deposited to explain the rhythmicity.

House (1985) has argued that the environmental fluctuations required under any of the interpretations to explain rhythmic or cyclic patterns is best met by changes in solar radiation and resultant changes in climatic patterns such as may be induced by orbital forcing due to changes in the Precession of the Equinoxes (21,000 year cycle), Obliquity of the Ecliptic (*ca.* 40,000 year cycle), Eccentricity of the Orbit (*ca.* 96,600 year cycle) and others. This type of control was first suggested for the Kimmeridge Clay patterns by Dunn (1974).

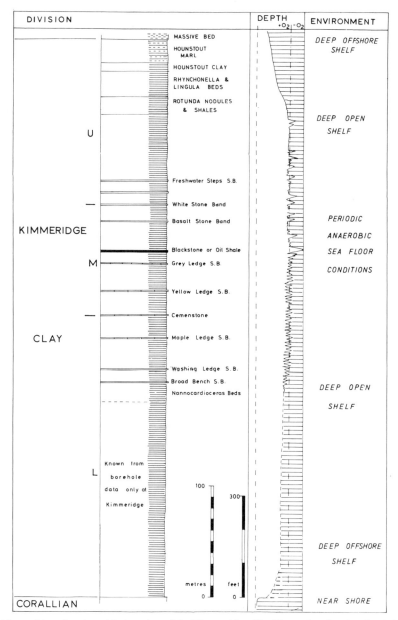

Figure 34.   Stratigraphical section of the Kimmeridge Clay Formation showing the main marker beds seen in the cliffs between Kimmeridge and Hounstout.

TABLE VIII. The Upper Kimmeridgian between Kimmeridge Bay and Hounstout (based on Cope 1967, Cope *et al.*, 1980b and Cox & Gallois, 1981).

Zone of Virgatopavlovia fittoni
Hounstout Marl 20.00m
Hounstout Clay 8.35
Rhynchonella and *Lingula* Beds (upper part) 8.00
Zone of *Pavlovia rotunda*
Rhynchonella and *Lingula* Beds (upper part) 15.00
Rotunda Shales 13.50
Rotunda Nodule Bed 1.80
Shales and Clays (Blake's Bed 2) 4.25
Zone of *Pavlovia pallasiodes*
Clays and Shales 30.00
Zone of *Pectinatites (Pectinatites) pectinatus*
Shales 6.10
Freshwater Steps Stone Band 0.38
Shales 8.80
Middle White Stone Band 0.36
Shales 8.83
White Stone Band 0.91
Zone of *Pectinatites (Arkellites) hudlestoni*
Shales 15.74
Basalt Stone Band 1.17
Shales 20.75
Cementstone 0.10
Shales 2.72
Rope Lake Head Stone Band 0.49
Shales 4.44
Blackstone 0.86
Zone of *Pectinatites (Virgatosphinctoides) wheatleyensis*
Shales and thin siltstones 19.25
Grey Ledge Stone Band 0.69
Zone of *Pectinatites (Virgatosphinctoides) scitulus*
Upper Cattle Ledge Shales 10.92
Cattle Ledge Stone Band 0.51
Lower Cattle Ledge Shales 15.67
Yellow Ledge Stone Band 0.46
Zone of *Pectinatites (Virgatosphinctoides) elegans*
Hen Cliff Shales 21.11
Cementstone 0.30
Shale 0.58
Cementstone (Blake's Bed 42) 0.20
Zone of *Aulacostephanus autissiodorense*
Maple Ledge Shales 27.00
Maple Ledge Stone Band 0.30
Gaulter's Gap Shales 25.00

Washing Ledge Stone Band 0.38
Washing Ledge Shales 15.00
Zone of *Aulacostephanus eudoxus* (pars)
The Flats Stone Band 0.46
Shales seen to 9.75

19A. Kimmeridge Bay (SY 908791). There is a car park on the cliff top. To the northwest is the Kimmeridge Oil Well of British Petroleum Co. Ltd. with a 'nodding donkey' for pumping oil up from the reservoir (Plate 25A). Production currently runs at about 350 barrels a day from a fissure system in the Cornbrash. The well has been in production since 1959 and total production by 1986 has been 2.7×10^6bbl. This is more than the original volumetric capacity of the reservoir (Stoneley and Selley 1986) so the reservoir is presumably being replenished by oil migration from lower levels. The succession in the original well was as follows (Brunstrom 1963):

Lower Kimmeridge Clay 0–243m
Corallian 243–340
Oxford Clay 340–519
Kellaways Beds 519–537
Cornbrash 537–564
Forest Marble and Fuller's Earth 564–889
Inferior Oolite 889–909
Bridport Sands 909–1042

A descent to the north can be made at Gaulter Gap and in the cliffs to the north simple ABAB rhythmicity is seen in beds above the Washing Ledge Stone Band which forms a ledge out to sea close to the Gap. Further northwest, and below the oil-well site, the Flats Stone Band forms a broad surface. This is cut by small thrusts which are thought to result from expansion of the original limestone as it became dolomitised (Bellamy 1977, Leddra *et al.*, 1987). This has led to the formation of small-scale ramp-flat thrusts (Ramsay 1991) (Plate 24).

Descending from the car park near the south end of the Bay the rhythmicity at ABAB level is seen where a stream cuts a small gully and the lithologies and fossil faunas can be examined. The kerogen-rich paper shales (unit B) are brown in colour and show vertical jointing. Near where the path joins the slipway, excavations have indicated the site of attempts to use the Kimmeridge Oil Shale industrially. John Clavell attempted to establish alum works in this area in 1570 and Sir William Clavell attempted alum works (1605) salt works (1610) and a glass factory (1618).

The cliff east of Clavell Tower is known as Hen Cliff and the sequence in it can be examined from below. The cliffs reach a culmination known as The Cuddle on the east side of which there is an obvious fault with a downthrow of 5.5m to the east. The Yellow Ledge Stone Band is about half way up the cliff below Clavell Tower and it sinks to shore level below The Cuddle to form a broad, well-jointed ledge. Local overthrusting (figured in Wilson 1980, Fig. 28, but given the wrong location) may be due to expansion of the unit during post-depositional dolomitisation. The Grey Ledge Stone Band is in the middle of the cliff at The Cuddle: the Blackstone enters at the top and descends slowly to the east and is marked by evidence of old adits. Efforts to work the Blackstone, or Kimmeridge Oil Shale, for oil extraction have all collapsed. The shale was used for ornaments in very early times. A fine sceptre of the material decorated with gold studs of the Bronze Age was found at Clandon Barrow (SY 656890) near Dorchester, and it occurs as decorations elsewhere. Finely carved furniture and other objects made from the Blackstone of Roman date and Iron Age bracelets are known. Good examples of these are in the Dorset County Museum (Itinerary 8E).

19B. Clavell's Hard (SY 920778). It is quickest to reach this locality by following the cliff-top path from the car park past Clavell's Tower and continuing to the east to the cliff-top at Clavell's Hard (Fig. 33). There a short descent can be made to an undercliff in the upper part of which is a prominent white limestone (0.5m thick), shown under the scanning electron microscope to be made of coccoliths (Plate 27B). This is the Rope Lake Head Stone Band. A small waterfall descends over the Blackstone or Kimmeridge Oil Shale (Plate 15, Fig. 34) and there is an adit in the Blackstone a few metres to the east. The pink colouration here results from a recent burning of the oil shale which continued for some years following a fire lit by schoolboys; it gave rise to spurious claims of spontaneous combustion (Plate 26A).

19C. East to Freshwater Steps. The foreshore beyond Clavell's Hard can be reached by a descent of the cliff just east of the adit at Clavell's Hard. This is usually perilous without a rope and stake. The cliffs and foreshore nearby display good sequences for examining all of the typical units of the Kimmeridgian rhythms and cycles. In the Blackstone and for 5m below it the pyritised free-living and planktonic crinoid *Saccocoma* is common, especially in the foreshore ledges 100m east of the descent. This crinoid, the petaloid pinnae of which are leaf-shaped and up to 8mm long, is found at only this level in boreholes throughout southern England: it is also common in the famous Solnhofen Limestone of southern Germany which is about the same age (Plate 26A).

For examination of the cliffs further east (Fig. 18d) it is valuable to have the account in the *Memoir* at hand and also the revisions of Cope (1967, 1978). It is even more important to have favourable tides. This area has produced many reptilian remains, including plesiosaurs, ichthyosaurs, crocodiles, chelonians and pterosaurs (Delair 1958–1960, Taylor and Benton 1986).

The so-called Basalt Stone Band (Figs. 33, 34), a cementstone unit, is well up the cliff where the Blackstone sinks beneath shore level, east of Clavell's Hard, and where it, in turn, reaches shore level, three white bands are prominent in the cliff (Plate 26B). The lowest of these, the White Stone Band, reaches the foreshore and is thrown up by a fault to descend again to the shore underneath the spur below Swyre Head. Large blocks of this laminated coccolith limestone, with evidence of contemporary-brecciation (Plate 27C), plant debris and the horizontal burrowing trace fossil *Rhizocorallium* form White Lias Rocks (Fig. 18d, Plate 18). The uppermost of the three bands is the Freshwater Stone Band which forms the base of the headland at the cascade at Freshwater Steps (SY 944773).

TABLE IX. The Portland Beds (Portland Limestone Formation) of the Isle of Purbeck coast. Details of the units based on Arkell (1947). The sequence refers to the St Alban's Head area and the Portland Stone sequence to Seacombe Quarries.

Portland Stone

SHRIMP BED	3.0m
TITANITES BED	3.0
POND FREESTONE	1.5
CHERT VEIN	1.5
LISTY BED	0.3
HOUSE CAP	2.6
UNDER PICKING CAP	0.9
UNDER OR BOTTOM FREESTONE	2.4

Cherty Series

Cherty limestones	ca. 11.0
PRICKLE BED OR PUFFIN LEDGE	0.46
Limestones with cherts	ca. 12.0
SEA LEDGES	5.2
Cherty limestone and sand	3.8

Portland Sand

THE BLACK SANDSTONES	6.7
THE PARALLEL BANDS	6.9
ST ALBAN'S HEAD MARLS	13.7
THE WHITE CEMENTSTONES	0.7
EMMIT HILL MARLS	9.1
THE MASSIVE BED	1.8

The cliff east of here gives a magnificent view of the whole western face of Hounstout. An ascent can often be made at this point, when a ladder is in place, and thence a return by the cliff-top path to Kimmeridge Bay.

20. CHAPMAN'S POOL AND ST ALBAN'S HEAD

For an excursion to Chapman's Pool the best starting point is from Kingston Matravers (SY 957796), 3km south of Corfe Castle (Fig. 38). However, because of deterioration of the cliff a former cliff-top car park is presently closed, necessitating a walk of 2.5km down the road and rough track south of Kingston to a point above the Pool (SY 956774). An alternative is to park a vehicle along the roadside 0.9km west of Worth Matravers and walk by the right-of-way which diverges from the St Alban's Head road 200m south of Renscombe Farm and crosses West Hill to give a steep descent to the Pool. The succession here and beyond St Alban's Head is summarised in Table IX.

20A. Hounstout Cliff (SY 951772) (Plate 28A). This fine cliff (Plate 28A) exposes a complete succession from the Freshwater Steps Stone Band seen on the west side at Freshwater Steps, up to the Portland Stone exposed on the crest of

Hounstout itself. The limits of the Hounstout Marl and Clay are indicated by seepages in suitable weather. The accessible lower cliffs around Chapman's pool expose the uppermost Kimmeridge Clay Pavlovia Zones and formerly fine specimens of the coarsely-ribbed ammonite *Pavlovia rotunda* were common from the Rotunda Nodules (Fig. 18), but they are rarer now, pending further cliff erosion.

20B. Pier Bottom (SY 958759). The sequence of the Portland Sand is best examined below Emmett's (or Emmit) Hill (SY 957763) just to the southeast. This can be approached by following the coast path south towards St. Alban's Head to within 200m of Pier Bottom (SY 958759), and then working back along the top of the scree slopes to the prominent Massive Bed. Beds below the Massive Bed have pavlovid ammonites and also *Zaraiskites* and *Epipallasiceras* (Cope 1970). The Emmit Hill Marls may yield the ammonites *Progalbanites* and *Epivirgatites* at about 3m below the White Cementstone. A simplified succession for the Portland Formation of this area is given on Figure 18d and Table IX, but for a detailed examination it is necessary to have at hand works by Arkell (1935, 1947), Townson (1975) and Wimbledon and Cope (1978) (Plate 28B).

20C. St Alban's Head (SY 961754). This can be visited either by continuing the walk via Pier Bottom (Fig. 18d) or via a return made to Kingston or Worth and using the deteriorating track to the lonely St. Aldhelm's Chapel (late 12th century). In the Portland Stone quarries at the Head mainly the Pond Freestone has been worked (the section given on Table IX applies to Seacombe). There is an ancient and rusty iron ladder for descent of the vertical cliff here for the intrepid which enables one to reach the blocks of fallen limestones at the foot of the cliff; this is a splendid area for adders and former geologists have recommended the use of gaiters (Plate 30A).

21. WINSPIT TO ANVIL POINT

There is a marvellous coastal path along these cliffs from Durlston Head to St. Alban's Head but access is difficult (Fig. 18e). Apart from walking from either end, access is by foot from Worth Matravers or Langton Matravers. The cliff-top path and cliffs are dangerous for children, especially in high winds. The chief interest is the development of the Portland Stone and lowest Purbeck Beds which form the cliffs and accounts of these beds have been published by Arkell (1935, 1947), Townson (1975) and West (1975) (Plate 30A, B).

21A. Winspit (SY 977761). The simplest approach to these cliff-top quarries is to follow the footpath down Winspit Bottom for 1.5km from Worth Matravers where there is very limited parking for a car 100m south-east of the church. At the cliff edge the Cherty Series forms the lower cliff and the Freestone Series, with galleries of former workings, forms the upper part (Table IX). At the top of the Portland Stone there is the Shrimp Bed, with the crustacean *Callianassa*. By walking north-east along the cliffs for one kilometre, Seacombe Quarries are reached and a similar sequence is exposed (and was described by Arkell in the *Memoir*). There is a public footpath up Seacombe Bottom for a return to Worth.

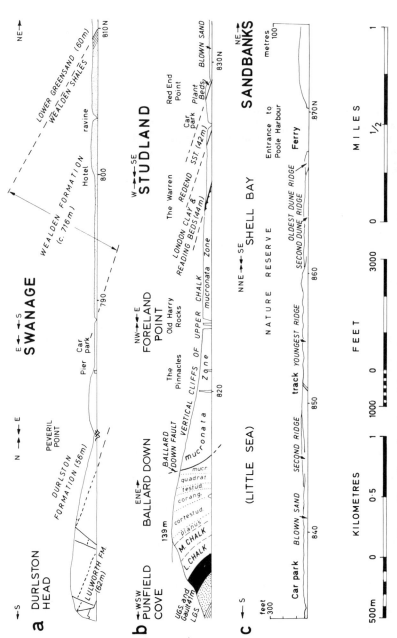

Figure 35. Coastal sections of the East Dorset coast from Durlston Head to Hengistbury Head. Vertical exaggeration ×3.

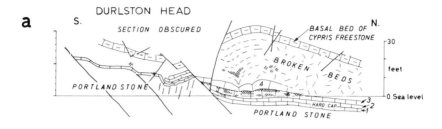

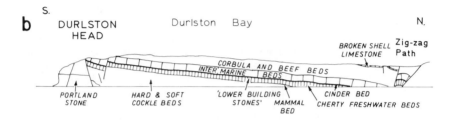

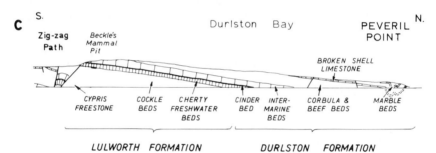

LULWORTH FORMATION   DURLSTON FORMATION

Figure 36.   Diagrams illustrating the geology of cliffs south-east of Swanage. a, Geology
of the lower cliff at Durlston Head and the southern part of Durlston Bay
(after West 1975). b, c, Cliff profiles of Durlston Bay illustrating the type
sequence of the Purbeck Beds (modified from Strahan 1898).

21B.   Langton Matravers (SY 999789). This village is 7.4km south-east of
Corfe and can also be easily approached from Swanage. St. James' Church shows
lavish use of polished Purbeck Marble installed during a rebuilding in 1875–6.
Behind the church is the excellent Coach House Museum with many exhibits of
the tools and methods of the local stone industry.

21C.   Dancing Ledge (SY 998769). From Langton, Durnford Drove leaves the
village 80m west of the church and the track continues as a footpath beyond
Spyway Barn to reach the cliff top at Dancing Ledge 2km away. There are old
quarry workings here, and also 0.5km farther west along the cliff, which show
similar sections to those at Seacombe (Table IX).

22. SWANAGE TO DURLSTON HEAD

The coast south-east of Swanage exposes the type section of the Purbeck Beds superbly and access is very easy. However, regular cliff falls in Durlston Bay have led to closure of the beach. Certainly it is wise only to work the section when the tide is low. There is no need to be close to the foot of the cliff. Falls often start disconcertingly from the top of the cliff, and out of sight. The sequence is documented in great detail (Clements 1969, 1993) and there are modern cliff profiles and maps for Durlston Bay (Nunn 1992) (Plate 30D).

The Purbeck Beds are widely developed in southern England and comprise shallow-water and well-bedded very pure limestones and shales thought to have been deposited in a broad lagoonal or lacustrine environment. Evaporation and salinity was often high, and this is indicated by evaporite deposits and by hypersaline algae and ostracods. North of Bedfordshire more fully marine sandy equivalents are known which are in part contemporaneous with the Speeton Clay of Yorkshire formed in the marine sea of the Boreal Realm. In the Dorset area local influxes of freshwater reduced the salinity to enable brackish or even freshwater molluscs (*Unio* and *Viviparus*) to be locally abundant. Marine influxes led to brackish-water conditions in which oysters could flourish. Exceptionally, in the Cinder Bed, are more fully marine indicators such as trigoniids, serpulids or even the echinoid *Hemicidaris*. Anderson (1985) recognised some marine or quasi-marine intercalations at other levels using a study of their microfauna. Shallow water is often indicated by desiccation cracks and dinosaur footprints (Delair 1960).

A good review of the faunas of the Purbeck Beds is given by Macfadyen (1970, p. 140–152). There are several levels with charales or stoneworts (Plate 25), an alga (Harris 1939), and a wide range of auracarian trees and cycadeoid tree-like seed-ferns, especially in the lower part (Francis 1983). The formation has yielded abundant gastropods (Arkell 1941), bivalves (Morter 1984) and insects (Hand-lirsch 1906–8), including beetles, cockroaches, grasshoppers and dragonflies. A checklist has been prepared by Jarzembowski (1991, 1993). Some 32 species of fish are known from the Swanage area (Woodward 1916–19), and crocodiles, tortoises and lizards occur. The dinosaurs include *Iguanodon* and perhaps *Stegosaurus* and *Megalosaurus* (Delair 1958–1960). A fine sequence of foot-prints of a bipedal dinosaur from Messrs J. & E.W. Suttle's pit at Hurston is set outside of the Natural History Museum, London, at the Exhibition Road entrance. At Sunnydown Farm (SY 982788), west of Langton Matravers, an area of excavated footprints is open to the public twice a year (information on times available from the Dorset Museum, Dorchester). Two megalosaurid trackways from Lock's Quarry, Langton, are exhibited in the Royal Scottish Museum (Delair 1980). The Mammal Bed has provided the best fauna of late Jurassic mammals in Europe (Clements, *in* House 1963) and includes herbivorous multituberculates, carnivorous Triconodonta, and symmetrodonts and probably tree-climbing pantotheres: none were larger than a fox, and mostly smaller. The fossils are found as small teeth with rarer jawbones. By 1970, according to Macfadyen, 93 specimens were known.

Models for the environment and palaeoecology of the Purbeck Beds as a whole envisage cycles of environmental change, often reflected in sedimentary cycles (West 1975), or microfossil (ostracod) cycles (Anderson 1985). Morter (1984) envisaged molluscan assemblages to range from fully marine (below) to freshwater (above) in the following sequence:

8. *Viviparus*, unionids
7. *Neomiodon medius*, *N. fasciatus*
6. *Neomiodon sublaevis*, *Ptychostylus*
5. *Myrene*, *Isognomon*
4. *Praeexogyra distorta*
3. *Myrene fittoni*, *Eocallista*, *Corbula*, *Modiolus*
2. *'Protocardia' major*
1. *Hemicidaris*, *Myophorella*, *Camptonectes*

Most of these forms have been illustrated in Morter's paper (1984).

The Purbeck limestones make good building stones, but the area is especially famous for the Purbeck Marble, a freshwater, *Viviparus*-rich limestone (Plate 29C) near the top of the succession. This takes a good polish (but is unmetamorphosed and hence not a true marble). The marble beds are biosparites full of *Viviparus*. These beds have been worked from Roman times (Beavis 1971). There are old adits along the dip slope from Swanage towards Worbarrow Bay. Their greatest use was in Mediaeval times (Dru-Drury 1948) as decorative piers, as seen in Durham (probably re-used for the Galilee Chapel from a collapsed former lady chapel, perhaps explaining the subsequent solely decorative use), Canterbury, and especially Salisbury cathedrals, and locally in St. Edmund's Chapel in Lady St. Mary Church, Wareham and, in the 19th Century, for St. James Church, Kingston. It was also used in Mediaeval times for fonts and characteristically flattened tomb-top figures, often of supposed crusaders (as, for example, the two cross-legged thirteenth century effigies in Lady St. Mary Church, Wareham). Terms used by Purbeck quarrymen have been reviewed by Arkell (1945).

22A. Peveril Point and Durlston Bay (SZ 040786). There is a large car park (SZ 035786) on the east side of Swanage from which a footpath passes eastward by the Hotel Grosvenor to the Lookout Post at Peveril Point. This is a convenient point to commence study of the type section of the Purbeck Beds in Durlston Bay to the south (Fig. 36b, 36c). The section will be described from the top downwards. There is an account of the section in the *Memoir* (Arkell 1947, p. 135–138) but the most detailed account is by Clements (1993, and *in* Torrens (Ed.), 1969) whose bed numbers are referred to in the text below; see also El-Shahat and West (1983). The succession given in Table VII is based on these authors.

Around Peveril Point itself the marble beds, near the top of the succession, can be examined without safety hazard. They are contorted into a W-shaped fold, and the two reefs out to sea reflect this. A Danish fleet is said to have been wrecked off these reefs in 876. Cosgrove and Hearn (1966) have shown that the structure is complex and they consider it a drag fold with minor thrusting. At the Point the detailed succession of the Upper Purbeck Beds of former use is as follows (the colours depend on the freshness of the rock section):

Shales above, not seen
Blue Marble (244) 1.0m
Red Marble 3.2
Shales (242) 3.2
Red Marble (241) with *Unio* abundant at the base 0.8
Shales (240) 1.8
Unio biosparite (239) 0.3
Green Marble (234−7) 0.45
Shales and thin limestones (221−233) 4.75
Broken Shell Limestone (220) below 2.8

The Broken Shell Limestone below is a hard, massive, cross-bedded, bioclastic limestone with *Neomiodon*, *Unio* and *Viviparus* with fragments of fish and turtles. This and higher beds are referred to the ostracod zone of *Cypridea setina*. The top of the Broken Shell Limestone is also seen, dipping *ca.* 16° north, below the Hotel Grosvenor. The upper surface has depressions on the surface, some over two metres across and 0.3m deep and suggestive of penecontemporaneous collapse structures.

Below the Broken Shell Limestone come the Middle Purbeck Beds, the highest unit of which is the Chief 'Beef' Beds (8m, Beds 190−219) mostly thin shaley limestones separated by shales, often paper shales with seams of 'beef' (fibrous calcite), and some selenite and the sulphur-weathering product jarosite. The ostracods (Plate 29A) are mostly *Cypridea*, *Darwinula* and *Theriosynoecum*. The 'Corbula' Beds (154−189) below (10.8m) comprise limestones (none exceeding one metre in thickness) and shales in approximately equal amounts. In the limestones of the top metre, gastropods are especially abundant (Arkell 1941) including *Hydrobia*, *Procerithium* and *Promathildia*. Below are the Scallop Beds (145−153), only 1.5m thick, but distinctive because of the occurrence of oyster, modiolid and pectenid bivalve shells indicating a more marine intercalation.

The Intermarine Beds (15.2m, Beds 112−144) include many limestones about one metre thick with generally thinner intervening shales. They yield brackish water faunas and have also fish and turtle remains. There are good levels for charales in the lower 2.5m (Plate 29B). This division was formerly and more appropriately called the Upper Building Stones: genetic terms such as 'Intermarine Beds' which give a subjective interpretation of the conditions of formation of a unit are inappropriate for stratigraphic terms.

The Cinder Bed (2.8m, Bed 111), forms the base of the Durlston Formation, and it is regarded as a marine incursion contemporaneous with the Ryazanian transgression of Russia and hence of basal Cretaceous date, although the actual level at which the Jurassic/Cretaceous boundary is to be drawn has yet (1993) to be internationally agreed. The Cinder Bed is a lumachelle (shell bed) full of *Praeexogyra distorta* and represents an oyster-shell bank which some consider widespread in southern England. At Durlston, the centre of the bed yields *Hemicidaris*, *Protocardia*, trigoniids and serpulids and there are lumachelles of the bivalve *'Protocardia' major* (Morter 1984) indicating the most marine facies in the Purbeck Beds. The trigoniid from this level has recently been named *Laevitrigonia cineris* by Kelly (1988).

The top unit of the underlying Lulworth Formation is the Cherty Freshwater Beds (8m, Beds 97–110). This comprises thin shales and thicker limestones, many of which contain black cherts, often with the gastropods *Hydrobia*, *Valvata* and *Viviparus*. This level has produced fine silicified specimens when dissolved in dilute hydrochloric acid and good naturally-etched specimens are known from field spoil around St. Alban's Head and other areas. The uppermost metre yields the first specimens of *Cypridea granulosa fasciculata* and the lower part has the zonal index *Cypridea granulosa granulosa*.

Below are the Marly Freshwater Beds (4m, Beds 75–86). These are calcarous and carbonaceous clays often with the gastropods *Hydrobia*, *Valvata* and *Viviparus*, and with charaleans in the lower part. The Mammal Bed appears to lie at about the middle of this unit. This level was formerly used to draw the boundary between the Lower and Middle Purbeck Beds of older terminologies. Mammals were first found by Brodie, a redoubtable collector, whose book on fossil insects (1845) includes much of interest for this section. Most of the known mammals came from Beckle's Pit dug around 1857, near the Zig-zag path (Fig. 36c). In recent years finds have been made on the foreshore below the zig-zag path itself (Heap 1957, Clements in House 1963).

The Soft Cockle Beds (22.3m, Beds 43–74) comprise micrites with subsidiary marls and shales in the upper third with halite pseudomorphs and moulds, often showing hopper faces. The middle portion includes thin limestones with serpulids, ostracods and hydrobiids. The lower third is of clays and well-laminated argillaceous micrites often with insect remains. In the lowest part there are masses of gypsum, formerly worked for making plaster-of-Paris.

The Hard Cockle Beds (3.7m, Beds 34–42) are more massive limestones and contain abundant bivalves. The underlying 'Cypris' Freestones (15.4m, Beds 10–33) include soft clays and marls; there are limestones in the lowest few metres which appear to be brecciated as in the Broken Beds at Durlston Point.

The section is almost completely repeated in the southern half of Durlston Bay by the faults which pass near the Zig-zag path (Fig. 36). Many parts of the succession are less clearly exposed but the preceding account should give a guide to horizons. An ascent can be made by the Zig-zag path to join Belle Vue Road, and a return made to the Swanage car park. If a descent is being made here, the path leaves Belle Vue Road between the flats of Purbeck Heights (nos 11–19) and Durlston Cliff beside an iron grill. Alternatively there is a cliff-top path to Durlston Head or the shore can be followed.

22B. Durlston Castle (SZ 034772). There is a large car park at the Durlston Country Park Centre. To the east is a steep cliff descent to the shore to the north of the Portland Stone globe (Plate 30C). The Broken Beds are best seen in the cliff east of Durlston Castle Café (Fig. 36a). Low water is needed. The Dirt Bed (0.3m), of black carbonaceous material with limestone fragments rests on the Portland Stone. In the Dirt Bed are rooted tree stumps: these and fallen trunks are silicified and thin sections show cell structure under the microscope. The Hard Cap (Beds 1 and 2 on Fig. 36a) and the caps above are noteworthy for the development in them of the strontium sulphate mineral celestine (these areas are cross-hatched on Fig. 36a, based on West 1960). Calciostrontianite also occurs (West *et al.*, 1969) (Plate 30C).

22C. Tilly Whim Caves (SZ 031769). These are 500m south-west of the Durlston County Park Centre car park. The Portland Stone has been worked in galleries here but these are not currently open to the public (Plate 30B).

23. SWANAGE BAY AND BALLARD DOWN

The coastal section from Swanage north to Foreland Point gives a sequence through the whole of the local Cretaceous. The succession comprises the Wealden Beds (about 750m), Lower Greensand (61m), Gault and Upper Greensand (48m) and the Chalk (about 400m). The Purbeck/Wealden junction is obscured. Exposures are generally poor along the foreshore of Swanage promenade but are very good further north.

23A. New Swanage (SZ 033800). By walking north along Swanage promenade a point is reached where the road diverges to the west and the cliffs begin. Descend here to the beach. The low cliffs for the next 1.4km expose in succession various lithologies of the Wealden described in the *Memoir* (Arkell 1947) and these include a range of alluvial deposits from sands and marls to shales, and with lignite and plant remains and occasionally *Unio* beds. When the Wealden Shales are reached in the northernmost part of the outcrop of the Wealden Beds there are shales and thin limestones, seen as blocks on the foreshore, with the ostracod *Cypridea*, the snail *Viviparus* and even oysters, indicating increased salinity.

23B. Punfield Cove (SZ 039810). This area can be reached by walking further north along the beach. It can be reached more quickly by following the road up the hill and parking as close to the coastal footpath as possible and finding a convenient descent to the shore. Formerly there was a good sequence of the Lower Greensand exposed in the cliff top (Fig. 37) and, although it is now much overgrown, a landslip may at any time expose it again. The sequence in recent years has been best known from the foreshore where Simpson (1983) has described the whole fauna anew, particularly the rich assemblages of the Punfield Marine Band (Cleeveley *et al.*, 1984) and demonstrated that the level is fully marine with a rich fauna of bivalves, gastropods (especially of the genus *Cassiope*) and several species of the ammonite *Deshayesites*. A cliff section and correlation of the Lower Greensand sequence with that in the Isle of Wight is given by Ruffell (1992).

The junction with the Gault is usually concealed but a basal bed of quartz pebbles is known. The Upper Greensand may be examined along the shore to the

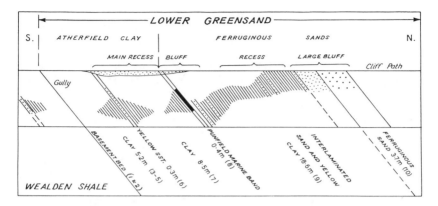

Figure 37.   Lower Greensand as formerly exposed in the cliff-top at Punfield Cove, Swanage. Bed numbers (of Arkell 1947) in parentheses (after House 1959).

north-east. The uppermost bed is a knobbly glauconitic sandstone (the Exogyra Rock) which contains the oyster, *Exogyra obliquata*, the echinoid, *Cardiaster* and the ammonite *Mortoniceras*. The Rock is capped by a phosphorite full of Albian fossils. A hard blue-grey stone band 8.5m below the top contains the ammonites *Anahoplites* and *Prohysteroceras*. Overslipped Chalk usually obscures much of this section.

The Lower Chalk here is about 31m thick. Details of the Chalk sequence are given by Rowe (1901) and Wright (*in* Arkell (1947). The Chalk Basement Bed contains the ammonites *Schloenbachia*, *Sciponoceras*, *Turrilites* and brachiopods. Fallen blocks from 12–15m higher contain small *Calycoceras*. The Plenus Marl, at the top of the Lower Chalk, contains ossicles of the starfish *Crateraster quinqueloba*. Only the two lowest zones of the Turonian (together constituting the bulk of the Middle Chalk) can be examined *in situ* before the cliffs become impassable on foot (a section is given by Mortimore and Pomerol 1987, p. 111). In the Labiatus Zone the zonal bivalve *Inoceramus labiatus* is abundant, especially in fallen blocks; spines of the echinoid *Tylocidaris* and tests of *Discoides dixoni* are common (recorded by Wright *in* Arkell 1947). The chalk of the Lata Zone is hard but yields the zonal brachiopod, *Terebratulina lata*. The overlying flinty Planus Zone can be examined in fallen blocks.

23C.   Ballard Down (SZ 045814). Little can be seen from the cliff-top walk to Foreland Point. However, during summer there are regular boat trips to Old Harry Rocks: it is now difficult to hire a boat for a special visit to the cliffs. This formerly provided the simplest way of seeing the extraordinary Ballard Down Fault (Fig. 35b) which cuts through the cliff a little north of Ballard Point. The fault plane curves listrically to the north, but on the southern, footwall side the Mucronata Zone chalk is vertical. The northern, hanging wall, side is also Mucronata Zone chalk but it dips and curves north concordantly with the fault plane. It is a puzzling feature and many theories have been proposed to explain it.

The structure of the Ballard Down Fault was first illustrated by Thomas Webster in an engraving dated 1815 (Plate 31C). A modern diagram of the structure is shown on Figure 38A (modified from Ameen and Cosgrove 1991). Clarke gave an early interpretation in terms of southward overthrusting (Fig. 38B). Jones and others (*in* Arkell 1947) favoured 'onion scale faulting' by which bedding slip led to frictional erosion of the foot wall (Fig. 38C). Arkell (1947) reviewed theories and illustrated an interpretation in which a low angle, northward dipping normal fault juxtaposed bedding concordant with the fault above the fault plane (Fig. 38D). Carter (1990) modified Clarke's interpretation to account also for a southern fault (F_1 on Fig 38A) and suggestsed the structures were late stage. Ameen and Cosgrove (1990, 1991) suggested that a northward overthrust ramp of chalk might have been rotated as a result of the reactivation of an underlying pre-Albian fault at depth (Fig. 38F). Unless a boat is specially hired, the easiest way to see the structures is to take binoculars on one of the regular summer boat trips to The Pinnacles or Old Harry Rocks.

24. WAREHAM, CREECHBARROW AND CORFE CASTLE

This area introduces the Tertiary succession which, although better seen on the coast, raises a number of fascinating problems (Fig. 35). There was a significant drop of sea level at the close of the Cretaceous and the early Tertiary Beds indicate this regression because in the Dorset area they are generally of non-marine or shallow-marine facies. There is a significant gap in the succession at the Cretaceous/Tertiary (or K/T) boundary and the Maastrichtian and much of the Palaeocene is missing. The environmental setting of the Dorset early Tertiary is of a low-lying tract with spreads of waterlain sands and grits and periods of lacustrine facies when clays were laid down, but the London Clay was mostly marine. Generally facies become more terrestrial and of coarser grade when traced westward along the Frome Valley. In the western area of Dorchester and Hardy's Monument mostly gravels are known, usually called the Bagshot Beds, and probably to be correlated with the Bournemouth Group (Table VI) of the east. To the southeast more marine facies are known in the Isle of Wight than in Dorset.

24A. Wareham (SY 923874). Wareham, established by Alfred the Great, forms the focus for routes into the Isle of Purbeck from the north. The Wytch Farm oilfield is only a few kilometres to the eastsoutheast (Locality 25C), but there are few exposures of solid rock. The best is at Redcliff (SY 932866), approached by following the Corfe road south from Wareham to Stoborough and taking the first left turn, and left after 0.6km to the lane which drops down to the River Frome. Here is a 30m cliff. The lowest 7.6m comprise red sands with a breccia of red clay clasts set in a matrix of red clay. Above are 6m of ferruginous sandstone, discordant with the breccias below, and followed by coarse sands with pebbles of quartz (Arkell 1947). It is thought that the upper units correlate with the Agglestone Grit (see later).

24B. Creechbarrow (SY 921824). The finest overview of east Purbeck, the Frome Valley, and the Wytch Farm oilfield is given from the top of

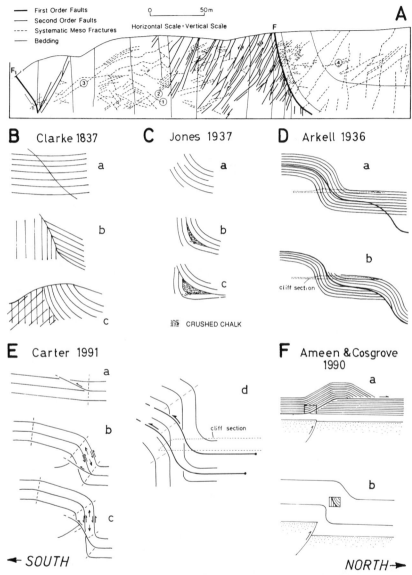

Figure 38.   Diagrams illustrating the structure and interpretation of the cliffs below Ballard Down. A, cliff profile (after Ameen and Cosgrove, 1991). B, a southward overthrust hypothesis (Clarke 1837). C, onion-scale faulting (Jones *in* Arkell 1947). D, low angle faulting (Arkell 1936). E, revised southward overthrusting (Carter 1991). F, overturned ramp structure (Ameen and Cosgrove 1990).

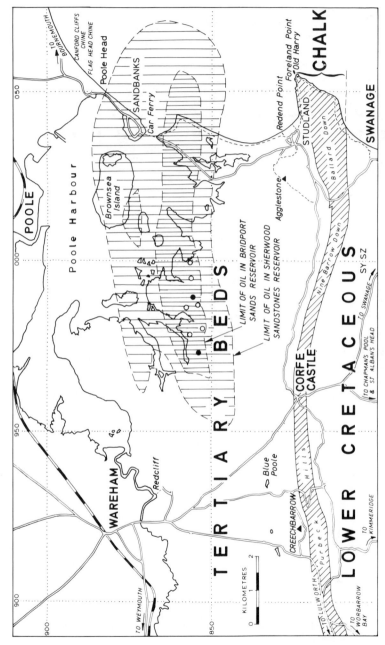

Figure 39.   Sketch map of East Dorset showing localities referred to in the text and the extent of reservoirs in the Wytch Farm oilfield.

Creechbarrow (Figs. 39, 40). There is parking beside a road on the south side. From here the conservationists may be surprised that they cannot even see the nodding donkeys of the notorious Wytch Farm Oilfield: they are hidden in the heath forests and give evidence of careful planning. Creechbarrow is an anomaly. It reaches a height of 194m, and rises above the supposed Miocene planation surface. It is higher than any of the Jurassic hills of the Isle of Purbeck, and higher than the summit ridge of the Chalk apart from Ridgeway Hill (198m) and Nine Barrow Down (199m). But it stands northward, apart from the Chalk ridge and is composed of Tertiary strata.

The relations of the Chalk of the middle limb of the Purbeck Monocline to the overlying Tertiary beds have been elucidated where the road from East Creech to Cocknowle crosses the Chalk ridge by a hairpin road between Stonehill Down and Knowle Hill to the east. Dips range from 70° north up to an inverted 99° south (Fig. 40), (Plate 31A). Yet excavations on Creechbarrow itself, and old dip records around East Creech, give only shallow dips of up to 12° north. Thus almost 213m of Tertiary strata could be accommodated between the top of the Chalk and the crest of Creechbarrow or even more if the Chalk/Tertiary boundary is faulted (Plint 1982). The succession so far elucidated, as given in the *Memoir*, is as follows:

UPPER CREECHBARROW BEDS
Creechbarrow Limestone 2–3m
Sand with bands of flint 6–9
MIDDLE CREECHBARROW BEDS
Buff brick-clay, flints at base *ca.*18
LOWER CREECHBARROW BEDS
Sand and coarse grit (thought to be equivalent of the
Agglestone Grit) 24–34
PIPE CLAY SERIES below

Hudleston, who did early excavations, and Arkell who followed him, preferred to use a local terminology rather than speculate on correlation with sections farther east, around Bournemouth. As a result of trenching, Hudleston found a varied molluscan freshwater fauna in a tufaceous Creechbarrow Limestone. L.R. Cox (*in* Arkell 1947) regarded these as indicative of the Bembridge Limestone of the Isle of Wight, that is, to be probably of Oligocene age. Hooker (1977, 1986) and Hooker and Insole (1980), on the other hand, consider the large mammal fauna of over forty species to be early Marinesian, and hence of middle Eocene age and equivalent to the Lower Barton Clay of Hampshire. This latter view has been adopted by Curry *et al.* (1978), who erected the Poole Formation for beds from the local top of the London Clay up to the Agglestone Grit (named after a coarse gravel-grit crag near Studland, Itinerary 25B) which has been taken to correlate with the Lower Creechbarrow Beds. Thus Curry *et al.* (1978), refer the Middle and Upper Creechbarrow Beds to the Bournemouth Formation (or Group).

This evidence of detailed age-dating is critical. At several levels within the Creechbarrow Beds flints occur which apparently could only be derived from erosion of the Chalk. Plint (1982) regards the earliest as late Lutetian. This would imply that the Purbeck fold may have been initiated in the Eocene rather than the Miocene date as is usually stated. Indeed, Small (*in* Jones (Ed.) 1980) has even proposed an Oligocene unconformity from the crest of Creechbarrow to the crest of Ridgeway. The new data make this improbable and since Oligocene strata are clearly involved in the Isle of Wight fold it seems likely that the Miocene movements were the greatest even if there is evidence for some earlier movement.

24C. Corfe Castle (SY 959824). This ancient royal fortress guarding the entrance to the Isle of Purbeck (Fig. 39) is basically Norman and was greatly strengthened in the 13th century but much wrecked by Parliamentarians in 1646 during the Civil War. An earlier Saxon structure is said to be where King Edward was murdered by his stepmother in 978. Double streams cut northward through the Chalk hogs-back to give the castle hillock and this is thought to result from drainage superimposition and downcutting (Plate 31B).

One kilometre north-west of the Castle are workings in the Pipe Clays of the early Bournemouth Group owned by ECC Ball Clays Ltd. (36 North Street, Warmwell) from whom permission to enter must be obtained. Older workings go west beyond Creechbarrow. Other pits still in operation are near Wareham and Arne.

25. STUDLAND BAY TO POOLE HARBOUR

This area may be reached either from Bournemouth using the Studland car and pedestrian ferry, or via Wareham and Corfe which is the best route from Weymouth (Figs. 1, 35, 38). It is the best area to study the early Tertiary sequence. The sequence is as follows :

BLOWN SAND forming sand dunes
PLATEAU GRAVELS mostly about 15m above OD.
POOLE FORMATION
   3. Agglestone Grit ; very coarse, pebbly and bedded
     grit .... 10.0+m
   2. Pipe Clay Series ; sands and clays with seams of
     pure plastic pipe clay .... 41.0+
   1. Redend Sandstone; red and yellow soft sandstone ..... ?42.7
LONDON CLAY FORMATION
   Sands with lignites, in total perhaps 26.0
READING FORMATION Sands and mottled and white
   clays with ironstones and basal flints, about 14.0

25A. Studland (SZ 044825). It is most convenient to use the South Car Park near the Bankes Arms Hotel (SZ 038825) and follow the short track in a narrow ravine to the shore. To the south are the Upper Chalk cliffs of the Mucronata Zone leading to Foreland Point. The basal Tertiary unconformity is accessible close to the corner. The Chalk surface is hummocky with hollows filled with ironstone and black flints. All of the Maastrichtian and the earliest Palaeocene are missing. The higher beds of the Reading Formation are mostly pale grey sands. At low

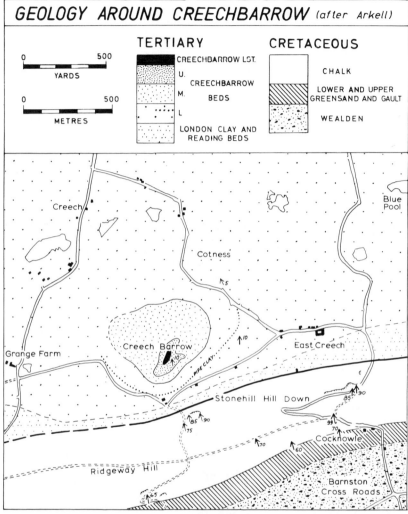

Figure 40. Geology of the area around Creechbarrow (modified from Arkell 1947).

water it is possible to work the Chalk at the foot of the cliffs all the way to Foreland Point.

Walking north along the shore, the London Clay Formation is mostly overgrown, but the yellow and red sands of the Redend Sandstone are well exposed up to Redend Point where there is piping of the upper surface. Overlying this are seen some 6m of grey sandy clay and sand with carbonaceous plant-remains.

25B.   The Agglestone (SZ 024828). This lies in the heath one kilometre north-
west of Studland and is most simply approached by the footpath west from
Studland Bay House. It comprises an isolated block of ferruginous gritstone, 6m
high and 18m in diameter, resting on a large mound of sandstones, presumably
of the Pipe Clay Series. The Puckstone, 300m northwest is a similar, but smaller
mass.

25C.   Wytch Farm (SY 978855). Development of the Wytch Farm oilfield
began in 1973 from an upper reservoir in the Jurassic Bridport Sands (Figs. 38,
40). In 1977 a lower reservoir was located in the Triassic Sherwood Sandstones.
In the early 1980's production was about 4000 and by 1984, 6000 barrels a day
and it was the largest onshore producing well in the country. Nevertheless, it is
planned to increase this production to 60,000 barrels of oil per day by exploiting
the lower field. This will also produce 10 million cubic feet of domestic gas each
day and 185,000 tonnes of liquefied petroleum gas per year. The field will then
be the largest onshore well in Europe. This will involve tapping reservoirs to the
east below Bournemouth Bay. Plans to do this by constructing on artificial island
in the Bay are now discarded and the reservoirs will be reached by feeder pipes
from the Wytch Farm field. The nodding donkeys at the surface may perhaps
be visited by arrangement with BP Petroleum Development Ltd., Wytch Farm,
Wareham.

The succession which has been established in the Wytch Farm boreholes
is indicated below (from Colter and Havard 1981). The range in thickness
values (which have been rounded) probably results from difficulties in precise
correlation and differences between boreholes:

TERTIARY
    Poole Formation 75m
    London Clay Formation 37
    Reading Formation 17–24
CRETACEOUS
    Upper Chalk 308
    Middle Chalk 58
    Lower Chalk 43
    Greensand, Gault and ?Lower Greensand 52
JURASSIC
    Oxford and Kellaways 132
    Cornbrash 8
    Forest Marble and Fullers Earth 165–178
    Inferior Oolite 0.6–2.7
    Bridport Sands 46–73
    Down Cliff Clay 152
    Junction Bed 15
    Middle Lias 15
    Lower Lias 61
TRIASSIC
    Penarth Group 21

Mercia Mudstone Group 349–365
Sherwood Sandstone Group 152
PERMIAN
  Aylesbeare Group 914
  Wytch Farm Breccias 61
(? DEVONIAN below).

The sequence is interesting in relation to the Winterborne Kingston Borehole 18km to the north-west (Dingwall and Lott 1979) where the Gault is unconformable on the lowest Kimmeridge Clay. Comparison shows a systematic thickening of all units from Wytch Farm. This suggests that the Triassic basin, inferred in the latter area, may have continued as a subsiding trough in at least the Jurassic. By contrast the Aptian and Albian appear to have thinned from the outcrops seen to the south in Punfield Cove, and in particular, the evidence for the Lower Greensand indicates only a small thickness. The Wealden Beds have been completely cut out by pre-Albian erosion. The Hercynian rocks encounted below the Permian are thought to be Middle or Upper Devonian.

The accompanying diagram (Fig. 41) is based on a description and illustration of the oil field by Colter and Havard (1981). It shows how the pre-Albian structure may have allowed oil to migrate into the present position from the south and west after maturation of oil shales in the Jurassic associated with their considerable depth at that time. Originally it was thought that the oil came from the Kimmeridge Clay, but current views favour a source in the Lias (Stoneley and Selley, 1986).

Figure 42 illustrates the background to the search for oil in this and other local areas. The preservation of oil-bearing spores and organic material is unusual, and mostly happens when the sea floor sediments are anoxic and normal biodegradation does not occur. Such conditions occurred in the early Lias, the early Oxford Clay and in Kimmeridge Clay times. These comprise the hydrocarbon source rocks of the area. The hydrocarbons are only forced out, as oils and gas, by considerable superincumbent sediment pressure and associated heat. Being lighter they migrate upwards until trapped, usually by a clay seal, in the pores of a reservoir rock. Appropriate depths are termed the maturation zone, or oil generation zone, usually taken to be betwen 15 and 160 on Lopatin's Time Temperature Index (TTI). The current disposition of the main source rocks are shown on Figure 42A. It will be seen on Figure 42B that it is only the Lower Lias which has been carried into the oil generation zone in East Dorset but it may be that higher source rocks in adjacent areas may have been lower and could source reservoirs in this area. A way in which the history of possible migration in an area can be analysed in shown on Figure 42C for three prospect areas. That for Wytch Farm (Fig. 42C(iii)) shows the sudden uplift associated with the regional mid-Cretaceous normal faulting. It was as a result of this faulting that oil accumulated in the Bridport Sands and, anomolously, in the Triassic Sherwood Sandstone.

25D. Studland Heath (SZ 037852). There are car parks at the south end (SZ 035835) and north end (SZ 035863) of Studland Heath Nature Reserve

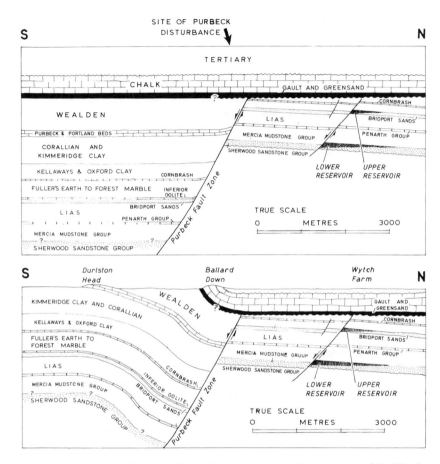

Figure 41.   Sections illustrating the geological evolution of the structure of the Wytch
              Farm Oilfield. Above, the early Tertiary structure showing the pre-Albian
              unconformity and faulting. Below, after the folding in the mid-Tertiary
              (modified from Colter and Havard 1981).

(Figs. 35c, 38), a centre of attraction for naturalists and, in summer, of naturists.
The heath is essentially of sand dunes, of pure white silica sand, devoid of
carbonates, derived mostly by long-shore drift from the Tertiary sandstone cliffs
to the east. Sometimes the sands are 'singing sands' when trodden underfoot. The
dunes are building eastwards and this is indicated by the three ridges parallel with
the coast which have developed since the sixteenth century. In 1721 Little Sea
(Fig. 35) was a tidal inlet. It has since been completely cut off from the sea.

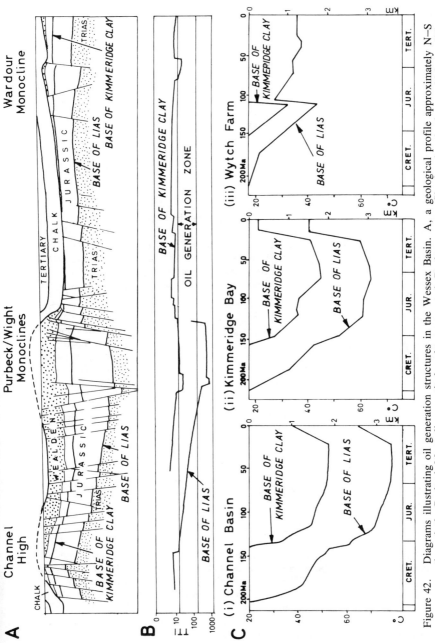

Figure 42. Diagrams illustrating oil generation structures in the Wessex Basin. A, a geological profile approximately N–S through the Purbeck Monocline, vertical scale exaggerated. B, the same profile showing depths to which possible source rocks have been depressed in relation to the oil generation zone. C, diagrams showing time/depth graphs for three areas. Modified from Stoneley and Selley (1986) and Penn et al. (1987).

26. POOLE, BOURNEMOUTH AND HENGISTBURY HEAD

The long length of low sand dunes and cliffs which stretches in a sweeping curve between Sandbanks, past Bournemouth, Boscombe and Southbourne to Hengistbury Head and the border with Hampshire exposes only early Tertiary rocks (Fig. 41). The lower beds are famous as the Bournemouth Plant Beds, the flora of which has been described by Chandler (1963). There is a scarcely discernible easterly dip. From Poole Head to Southbourne there is a fine promenade below the cliffs giving ready access everywhere. In summer, alas, the area is one of the most densely populated with negligibly-clad humanity in Europe, and is best avoided. Parking for cars in summer is very difficult. Furthermore, the cliffs are freely decorated with notices forbidding climbing, or access, and very long stretches are behind fences or long terraces of beach huts. Now the promenade is virtually complete, and with groynes every few hundred metres, cliff erosion is at a minimum and revetting, grassing-over, and 'improving' will before long conceal all but the largest outcrops. The regions where exposures are currently to be seen are marked on Fig. 41. Some of the exposures here are quite spectacular, especially sections west of Branksome Chine, west of Alum Chine, east from Bournemouth Pier and west from Branscombe Pier. Hengistbury Head for a half day stroll gives an admirable overview of the eastern end of Dorset and less favoured regions farther to the east.

The coast is famous for its 'chines', or deeply-cut gorges in the Tertiary sands, usually cut at right angles to the coast. Some, such as Alum and Branksome Chines, show an upper, wider valley, into which is cut a narrower chine graded to the present beach. This has led to the suggestion that some are developed from more ancient streams which drained into the ancient 'Solent River' (Bury 1920). Some chines are of a smaller scale and have developed where clay seams have given rise to local seepages and backcutting erosion.

The general geological succession in the area is best revealed by the Christchurch Borehole (SZ 20029301) sunk to a total depth of 318.5m (for reference, see I.G.S. 1983):

PLATEAU GRAVEL 2.5m
BARTON CLAY 7.7
BOURNEMOUTH GROUP 221.2
LONDON CLAY FORMATION 67.1
READING FORMATION 19.9

The London Clay and Reading Beds are not exposed here. The Eocene Bournemouth Group is divided into the Poole Formation below and the Bournemouth Formation above. The latter is seen in the cliffs and comprises succeeding units of Bournemouth Freshwater Beds (? 70m), Bournemouth Marine Beds (ca. 20m ?), Boscombe Sands (ca. 10m) and Hengistbury Beds (15m): these are seen from oldest to youngest in the west to east traverse from Poole Head to Hengistbury Head. The early descriptions of Gardner (1879, 1882) written over a century ago are now superseded by the account in the new Bournemouth *Memoir* (Bristow et al., 1991).

The new *Memoir* introduces a new terminology in which the Poole Formation is subdivided into several subdivisions using marker clay levels (the Creekmore, Oakdale, Broadstone and Parkstone Clays). The early Bournemouth Freshwater Beds and Bournemouth Marine Beds are combined as the Branksome Sand which, with the Poole Formation they term the Bracklesham Group. The Boscombe Sands and higher beds are combined as the Barton Group. The new terminology is marked on the coastal profiles (Fig. 43).

26A. Sandbanks (SZ 038870). Where the ferry leaves for Studland, there is a slight promontory (Fig. 41a). It is now largely built over and around so that little trace of bedrock is visible and only evidence of sand dunes is seen. About 350m east of the ferry pier, and 100m beyond Salter Road on the one-way road system, Midway Path leads to the shore. Only windblown sands are seen where the sea defences allow, but the foreshore is often a good place to gather the recent shells which indicate the molluscs living on the offshore sandflats. These include the epibenthonic snail *Crepidula fornicata*, often with mounting shells in life position, the oyster, *Ostrea edulis* and the mussel, *Mytilus edulis*, as well as burrowing endobiont suspension feeders such as the razor shell, *Ensis ensis*, *Mya arenaria*, *Astarte sulcata*, *Acanthocardia* and others in lesser abundance.

At the extreme western end of Sandbanks car park (SZ 044875) many large blocks of Purbeck and Portland limestone have been placed to protect the north side of day chalets. Some trace of gravels largely obscured by blown sand is seen.

26B. Lilliput (SZ 042892). Where the Sandbanks to Poole road rises from the flats of the blown sand area, at the East Dorset Sailing Club, a coastal path diverges along the foot of the cliff and for the next 200m are poor exposures of the Bournemouth Freshwater Group with sands and gravels (Bagshot Beds type) with chert gravels of the Plateau Gravels slipped from above. Where the path terminates to the northwest is a path back up to the road.

26C. Poole Head (SZ 051883). This is the start of the coastal promenade and there is a small car park close to the shore. From here there is an agreeable stroll eastward but with very few outcrops of sands of the Bournemouth Freshwater Group, as on the western side of Flag Head Chine where the fossil remains of laurel, hornbeam and willow were recorded by Gardner (1882), and on Canford Cliffs where cliff climbing is prohibited and a gravel capping can be seen at the cliff top.

26D. Branksome Chine (SZ 065897). This is the best excursion for a short visit. At the mouth of the chine is a car park. Often on the foreshore hereabouts can be found blocks of lignite, sometimes bored by *Teredo*, washed out of the offshore beds. After walking 500m west there is an excellent exposure through the whole cliff of yellow and orange sands of the Bournemouth Freshwater Beds, with large-scale cross bedding and a capping of Plateau Gravel seen at the cliff-top towards Canford Cliffs Chine. Access to the section requires permission. It may be more convenient to approach this outcrop from Cliff Gardens and by descending the cliff path and walking a lesser distance westward (Fig. 41a).

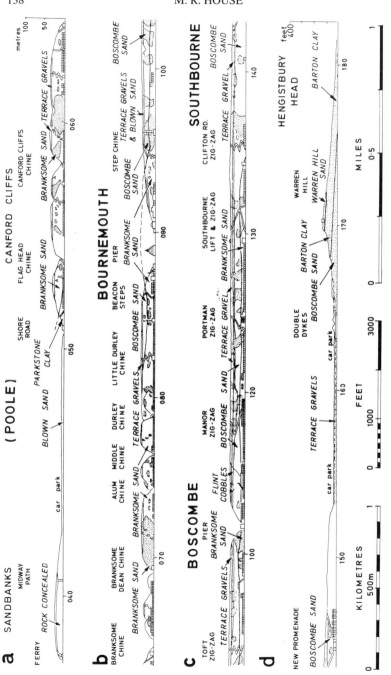

Figure 43.   Cliff profiles showing the geology of the east Dorset coast between Sandbanks and Hengistbury Head. Areas of present exposures of solid rocks are stippled. Vertical exaggeration ×3.

The walk east from Branksome Chine is also worthwhile (Fig. 41b) for showing facies of the Bournemouth Freshwater Beds. There is a wall of ferruginous sandstone just before the chalets begin. The low cliffs from here to Branksome Dene Chine were formerly good exposures of the plant beds (Gardner 1882). These are now best seen in the laminated pink and grey cross-bedded silts, sands and clays with leaf beds just east of Branksome Dene Chine where there is another fine cliff section. Again bored lignite blocks can be found on the shore.

26E.   Alum Chine (SZ 074902). This is not so satisfactory an access point unless it is used to approach the exposures referred to above east of Branksome Dene Chine. Between Alum Chine and Middle Chine are scrappy exposures in the cliffs which are difficult to approach. There are other exposures east of Great Durley Chine (where there is a small car park) and formerly these cliffs showed leaf beds, lignitic sands with *Teredo*-bored lignitic wood, palm remains and there was a *Myrica* (myrtle) bed reported (Gardner 1882) high in the cliff between Great Durley Chine and Little Durley Chine. There is access to the cliff top by the West Cliff Zig-zag path (Fig. 41b).

26F.   Bournemouth Pier (SZ 089906). At 400m west of the Pier there is a fine 12m section of mauve clays overlain by yellow sands seen either side of the cliff railway. These include beds of ferns, *Gleichenia* and rolled leaves noted by Gardner (1882).

East from the Pier the Geological Survey drew the local boundary between the Bagshot and overlying Bracklesham Beds where evidence of a 'marine' fauna was first seen in the upper cliff east of Step Chine, 900m east of the Pier. Gardner (1879) argued that the marine beds here passed laterally into those of freshwater origin. But the 'marine beds' are recognised mostly by oysters which are not an indicator of fully-marine conditions.

At present there is an exposure of 10m of orange sand with a 1m white band near the top about 400m east of the Pier. Step Chine is now the site of a zig-zag path to the cliff top and there is a good exposure of plant beds and grey clays in buff sands in the lower part of the cliff on the west side. At 150m to the east is a cliff railway and on both sides there are excellent exposures in the cliffs, albeit mostly not readily reached, but comprising some 30m of orange and white sands with large scale cross bedding. Plateau Gravels cap the cliff and the foreshore here is strewn with chert, flint, ironstone and sandstone cobbles probably mostly derived from Plateau Gravels at the cliff top. About 200m further east can be seen the tripartite division of the cliff into gravels at the top, white Boscombe Sands in the middle, and usually grey silts of the Bournemouth Marine Beds at the base. This tripartite division characterises the cliff section to the east to Boscombe Pier.

26G.   Boscombe Pier (SZ 112911). Undercliff Drive, west from the Pier, is usually open to vehicles out of the holiday season and so it is possible to drive almost to Bournemouth Pier (where there is no exit). Thus, this is the easiest approach to the sections east of Bournemouth Pier. Apart from the interesting western sections already described, however, the section is similar all the way along and comprises the tripartite arrangement of terrace gravels at the top, white sands, and finely laminated grey and buff silts of the Bournemouth Marine Beds at the base. The lower part is especially well seen immediately west of Boscombe Pier. There is an easy descent of East Cliff by Toft Zig-zag from Manor Road or Easy Overland Drive opposite Manor Road and there are other sections half way between here and Boscombe Pier.

East from Boscombe Pier the undercliff promenade is not open to traffic and access is not so easy. The Bournemouth Marine Beds are not recorded here except close to Boscombe Pier. The sequence in the Boscombe Sands can be seen by descending any of the cliff paths. The descents are, Manor Zig-zag from Boscombe Overcliff Road opposite Grovely Avenue, the Portman Zig-zag from opposite Ravine Road, or the Southbourne Zig-zag from opposite the Commodore Hotel. Present exposures are shown on Figure 41c.

26H.   Hengistbury Head (SZ 178904) (Plate 32A,B). There is car parking near Double Dykes (SZ 163909) and a cliff walk to the east towards the Head. There are good exposures along the southern and western side of the headland (Fig. 41d). The succession comprises equivalents of the Barton Beds to the east overlain by Plateau Gravels. Curry (1976) has elucidated the following succession (at SZ 175905) (Plate 34).

PLATEAU GRAVELS above
HIGHCLIFF SANDS
    7. Slightly laminated sands, pale yellow above with *Solen*
       and *Panopea*, and grey below with *Pinna* 10.0m
HENGISTBURY BEDS
    6. Brown and grey stiff clays with layers of
       fine sand 3.0
    5. Grey-brown fine sandy clay with some glauconite. With
       abundant moulds of molluscs associated with nodules.
       Nummulites rectus occurs 7.3
    4. Very glauconitic grey-green clayey fine sand with some
       quartz grit.
       Nummulites prestwichianus occurs 4.0
    3. As above but sands more coarse-grained. Quartz grit
       abundant in the lower part and with a band of flint-
       pebbles up to 15cm at the base 5.5
BOSCOMBE SANDS
    2. Buff and chocolate coloured sands with curved bedding
       planes marked by scattered small pebbles 5.0
    1. Lignitic sands and clays at base of cliff, seen to 2.0

Curry (1976) has established a correlation between the Hengistbury section and the better-known Bartonian sections at Highcliffe, east of Christchurch and in Hampshire. A detailed list of molluscs identified from these beds has been recorded by Hooker (1975).

MAPS, MEMOIRS AND OTHER GUIDES

Dorset is well covered by available maps. The modern topographical maps have the advantage of showing the public rights of way. This guide has used the National Grid References widely in the text so small scale maps would be very useful to use with this guide even though grid references are shown on most of the diagrams. In the National Grid System 100km squares are designated by letters (as SY and SZ on Fig. 1a). In the the six-figure reference, the first three figures gives distance in tenths of a kilometre east (eastings) from the south-west corner of the 100km square and the second three figures gives the distance north (northings) from the same corner. Eight figure references give distances in hundredths of a kilometre and are useful mainly on larger scales than 1:10,000.

1. TOPOGRAPHIC MAPS

The coastal area of Dorset is covered by the following 1:50,000 Ordnance Survey Landranger Maps of East Devon and Dorset:

Sheet 193 Taunton and Lyme Regis
Sheet 194 Dorchester and Weymouth
Sheet 195 Bournemouth

The area is covered by the following 1:25,000 Ordnance Survey Maps of the Pathfinder Series or Second Series. The limits of these maps are shown by the grid on Fig. 1:

Sheet SY 29/39 Lyme Regis and Axminster
Sheet SY 49/59 Bridport
Sheet SY 58 Abbotsbury
Sheet SY 68/78 Weymouth (North)
Sheet SY 67/77 Weymouth and Portland
Sheet SY 88/98 Wareham and West Lulworth
Sheet SY 87/97, SZ 07 Swanage and Kimmeridge
Sheet SZ 08 Studland
Sheet SZ 09/19 Bournemouth

The area of the last four sheets is mostly covered on the single sheet of the 1:25,000 *Outdoor Leisure Map of Purbeck* which is the better buy.

2. GEOLOGICAL MAPS

The following maps of the British Geological Survey (formerly the Institute of Geological Sciences) are available at the scale of 1:50,000 or, in the older editions and only available secondhand, at one inch to the mile.

Sheet 326/340 Sidmouth (and Lyme Regis)
Sheet 327 Bridport
Sheet 328 Dorchester
Sheet 341/342 West Fleet and Weymouth
Sheet 343 Swanage
Sheet 329 Bournemouth

3. BRITISH GEOLOGICAL SURVEY PUBLICATIONS

The most important of these are as follows; details are given in the References which follow. For the *Memoirs* the areas referred to are those of the one inch to the mile and 1: 50,000 Geological Sheets listed above.

The geology of the country near Sidmouth and Lyme Regis
(Woodward and Ussher 1911).

Geology of the country around Bridport and Yeovil
(Wilson *et al.* 1958).

Geology of the country around Weymouth, Swanage, Corfe and Lulworth
(Arkell 1947. Addenda and Corrigenda have been added with subsequent reprintings).

Geology of the country around Dorchester
(Reid 1899).

The geology of the country around Bournemouth
(Reid 1898). 2nd Edition (Bristow *et al.*, 1991) with accompanying revised Sheet 329 (1991)

The Hampshire basin and adjoining areas
(Melville and Freshney 1982).

Bristow (1993) has published a review of the large number of BGS reports available since 1969 relating to Dorset Geology mostly referring to inland areas.

4. OTHER GUIDES

The Geologists' Association has published earlier guides to the Dorset coast (Ager and Smith 1959, House 1958, 1969). The area has been visited on many occasions by the Association on field excursions and field reports are mentioned in the text. Particularly noteworthy are those reported by Carreck (1960), Jarvis and Tocher (1987), Sellwood *et al.* (1970), Sylvester-Bradley (1948), and West *et al.* (1969). Ten-year surveys of literature on Dorset geology were published by Arkell (1951b) and House (1963).

An excellent general guide but now out-of-date in many matters is that by Davies (1935, 1956). Specialist guides include one for an International Field Symposium on the British Jurassic (Torrens, Ed., 1969), a guide for petroleum geologists (Stoneley and Selley 1986), a guide for geomorphologists (Brunsden and Goudie 1981), a guide for micropalaeontologists (Lord and Bown (Eds.) 1987) and a report on Tertiary localities (Hooker 1975). An excellent guide to Nature Conservancy sites is by Macfadyen (1970). A guide for sedimentologists was produced for the 13th International Sedimentological Congress (Sellwood and Wilson 1990). Coastal landforms of West Dorset are covered in a recent guide published by this Association (Allison (Ed.) 1992). Full details of these are given in the references.

The Palaeontological Association has commenced a series of illustrated guides to fossils of British formations. The following relevant guides have so far been published. *Fossils of the Oxford Clay*, Ed. D.M. Martill and J.D. Hudson (1991); *Fossils of the Chalk*, E. Owen and A.B. Smith (1987); *Fossil plants of the London Clay*, M.E. Collinson (1983).

A full bibliography of literature relating to Dorset geology up to 1989 has been published (Thomas and Ensom 1989) which is more comprehensive than the references given here.

TIDES AND OTHER HAZARDS

1. TIDES

The times of high and low water at Portland are usually given in the quality daily papers and local tide tables are available from chandlers, fish-tackle shops and some local newsagents. The *Admiralty Tide Tables* published each year by the Hydrographer of a Navy are a primary source for information.

The tides at Lyme Regis are approximately sinusoidal, but at Portland there is the start of 'double tides' with a double low water, and east of Swanage this has become a double high tide. Predictions usually quote the first 'low' or 'high'. Most of the coast can be worked at neap tides, which occur approximately two weeks after new moons, when the tidal range is at its lowest. At Portland the mean range at springs is 1.9m and at neaps 0.7m, but at the equinoxes the range is greater. High tide at Portland occurs at about 7 o'clock on the first day of a new moon and is then about 50 minutes later each day. Tides at Lyme Regis are about half an hour earlier and at Swanage the first high tide is about 90 minutes later than on Portland. This guide has sufficient appropriate inland exposures mentioned to avoid time loss during periods of inclement tides or weather.

2. HAZARDS

The biggest hazard along the Dorset coast is from fragments falling with increasing velocity from above. Many fatalities are known. Below all stretches with steep or vertical cliffs hard hats are necessary. Climbing on cliffs is also a cause of death each year. These factors are even more hazardous after rains. In western areas near Lyme Regis and Charmouth landslips can also be dangerous at such times. The tides can be an inconvenience, restricting access, or in some cases swamping it, and it can necessitate a patient wait for the ebb often in a barely comfortable place. In certain places cliff-top paths are dangerous in windy weather.

REFERENCES

Ager, D.V. 1956–1967. A monograph of the British Liassic Rhynchonellidae. *Palaeontogr. Soc.* **176,483,498,519,** xxxvi, 172pp, 13 pl.

Ager, D.V. and Smith, W.E. 1965. The Coast of South Devon and Dorset between Branscombe and Burton Bradstock. *Geologists' Association Guide No.* **23**, 21pp.

Allison, R.J. (ed.). (1992) *The coastal landforms of West Dorset. Geologists' Association Guide No.* **47**, 134pp.

Ameen, M.S. 1990. Macrofaulting in the Purbeck–Isle of Wight monocline. *Proc. Geol. Ass.* **101**, 31–46.

Ameen, M.S. and Cosgrove, J.W. 1990a. A kinematic analysis of the Ballard Fault, Swanage, Dorset. *Proc. Geol. Ass.* **101**, 119–129.

Ameen, M.S. and Cosgrove, J.W. 1990b. A kinematic analysis of mesofractures from Studland Bay, Dorset. *Proc. Geol. Ass.* **101**, 303–314.

Ameen, M.S. and Cosgrove, J.W. 1992. An upper strain detachment model for the Ballard Fault : reply. *Proc. Geol. Ass.* **102**, 315–320.

Anderson, F.W. 1985. Ostracod faunas in the Purbeck and Wealden of England. *Micropalaeont.* **4**, 1–68.

Anderson, F.W. and Bazley, R.A.B. 1982. The Purbeck Beds of the Weald (England). *Bull. geol. Surv. G.B.* **34**, 174pp.

Andrews, J. 1988. Soil–zone microfabrics in calcrete and in desiccation cracks from the Upper Jurassic Purbeck Formation of Dorset. *Geol. Jl* **23**, 261–270.

Arber, M.A. 1973. Landslips near Lyme Regis. *Proc. Geol. Ass.* **84**, 9–133.

Arkell, W.J. l933. *The Jurassic System in Great Britain.* Clarendon Press, Oxford. xii, 681pp, 41 pl.

Arkell, W.J. 1935. The Portland Beds of the Dorset mainland. *Proc. Geol. Ass.* **46**, 301–347.

Arkell, W.J. 1936. The Corallian Beds of Dorset. *Proc. Dorset Nat. Hist. arch. Soc.* **57** (for 1935), 59–93, 4 pl.

Arkell, W.J. 1940. Dorset Geology, 1930–1940. *Proc. Dorset nat. Hist. arch. Soc.* **61** (for 1939), 117–135, 1 pl.

Arkell, W.J. 1941. The gastropods of the Purbeck Beds. *Q. Jl geol. Soc. Lond.* **97**, 79–128.

Arkell, W.J. 1945. The names of the strata in the Purbeck and Portland Stone quarries. *Proc. Dorset nat. Hist. archaeol. Soc.* **66** (for 1944), 158–168.

Arkell, W.J. 1947. *The geology of the country around Weymouth, Swanage, Corfe and Lulworth.* Mem. geol. Surv. G.B. xii, 386pp, 19 pl.

Arkell, W.J. 1948. Oxford Clay and Kellaways Beds, Weymouth. *Proc. Dorset nat. Hist. archaeol. Soc.* **69** (for 1947), 122–124.

Arkell, W.J. 1951a. The structure of the Spring Bottom Ridge and the origin of the mud slides, Osmington. *Proc. Geol. Ass.* **62**, 21–300.

145

Arkell, W.J. 1951b. Dorset Geology, 1940–1950. *Proc. Dorset nat. Hist. arch. Soc.* **72** (for 1950), 176–194, 2 pl.

Aubrey, M.P., Hailwood, E.A. and Townsend, H.A. 1986. Magnetic and calcareous-nannofossil stratigraphy of the Lower Paleogene formations of the Hampshire and London Basins. *Jl. geol. Soc. Lond.* **143**, 729–735.

Barber, K.E. (Ed.) 1987. *Wessex and Isle of Wight Field Guide.* Quaternary Research Assoc. Field Guide.

Barker, D., Brown, C.E., Bugg, S.C. and Costin, J. 1975. Ostracods, land plants and charales form the basal Purbeck Beds of Portesham Quarry, Dorset. *Palaeontology* **18**, 419–436.

Beavis, J. 1971. Some aspects of the use of Purbeck Marble in Roman Britain. *Proc. Dorset nat. Hist. archaeol. Soc.* **92** (for 1970), 181–204.

Bellamy, J. 1977. Subsurface expansion megapolygons in an Upper Jurassic dolostone (Kimmeridge, U.K.). *Jl sediment. Petrol.* **47**, 973–978.

Bristow, C.R., Freshney, E.C. and Penn, I.E. (1991). *Geology of the country around Bournemouth.* British Geological Survey, HMSO, 116pp.

Bristow, C.W. 1993. Recent work of the British Geological Survey in Dorset. *Proc. Dorset nat. Hist. archaeol. Soc.* **114** (for 1992) 207–214.

Brodie, P.B. 1845. A history of the fossil insects in the Secondary rocks of England. *J. van Voorst, London.* xvi, 130pp, 2 pl.

Brookfield, M.E. 1970. Eustatic changes of sea level and orogeny in the Jurassic. *Tectonophysics* **9**, 347–363.

Brookfield, M.E. 1973. The palaeoenvironment of the Abbotsbury Ironstone (Upper Jurassic) of Dorset, *Palaeontology* **16**, 261–274.

Brookfield, M.E. 1978. The lithostratigraphy of the upper Oxfordian and lower Kimmeridgian Beds of South Dorset, England. *Proc. Geol. Ass.* **89**, 1–32.

Brunsden, D. and Jones, D.K.C. 1976. The evolution of landslide slopes in Dorset. *Phil. Trans. R. Soc. Lond.* **A 283**, 605–631, pl. 12–13.

Brunsden, D. and Goudie, A. 1981. *Classic coastal landforms of Dorset.* Geograph. Assoc., Landform Guides, No. 1, 39 pp.

Brunstrom, R.G.W. 1963. Recently discovered oilfields in Britain. *6th World Petrol. Congress, Sect. 1, Pap. 49,* 11–20.

Bujak, J.P., Downie, C., Eaton, G.L. and Williams, G.L. 1980. Dinoflagellate cysts and acritarchs from the Eocene of southern England. *Spec. Pap. Paleontol.* **24**, 100pp.

Bryant, I.D., Kantorowicz, J.D. and Love, C.F. 1988. The origin and recognition of laterally continuous carbonate-cemented horizons in the Upper Lias Sands of southern England. *Marine & Petroleum Geology* **5**, 108–133.

Bury, H. 1920. The chines and cliffs of Bournemouth. *Geol. Mag.* **57**, 71–76.

Bury, H. 1933. The plateau gravels of the Bournemouth area. *Proc. Geol. Ass.* **44**, 314–334.

Carr, A.P. 1969. Size grading along a pebble beach; Chesil Beach, England. *Jl sedim. Petrol.* **39**, 297–311.

Carr, A.P. and Blackley, M.W.L. 1969. Geological composition of the pebbles of Chesil Beach, Dorset. *Proc. Dorset nat. Hist. archaeol. Soc.* **90** (for 1968), 133–140.

Carr, A.P. and Blackley, M.W.L. 1973. Investigations bearing on the age and development of Chesil Beach, Dorset, and the associated area. *Trans. Inst. Br. Geogr.* **58**, 99–111.

Carr, A.P. and Blackley, M.W.L. 1974. Ideas on the origin and development of Chesil Beach, Dorset. *Proc. Dorset nat. Hist. archaeol. Soc.* (for 1973). **95**, 9–17.

Carreck, J.N. 1960. Whitsun Field Meeting to Weymouth, Abbotsbury and Dorchester, Dorset. *Proc. Geol. Ass.* **71**, 341–347.

Casey, R. 1961. The stratigraphical palaeontology of the Lower Greensand. *Palaeontology* **3**, 487–621.

Carter, D.C. 1992. An upper strain detachment model for the Ballard Fault : a discussion. *Proc. geol. Ass.* **102**, 309–315.

Chadwick, R.A. 1986. Extension tectonics in the Wessex Basin, southern England. *Jl geol. Soc., Lond.* **143**, 465–488.

Chadwick, R.A. 1993. Aspects of basin inversion in southern Britain. *Jl geol. Soc. Lond.* **150**, 311–322.

Chandler, M.E.J. 1960. Plant remains of the Hengistbury and Barton Beds. *Bull. Brit. Mus. nat. Hist. (Geol.)* **4**, 191–238, pl. 29–35.

Chandler, M.E.J. 1962. *The Lower Tertiary Floras of Southern England. Part 2: Flora of the Pipe-clay series of Dorset.* Brit. Mus. nat Hist., London. v, 176pp, 29 pl.

Chandler, M.E.J. 1963. *The Lower Tertiary Floras of Southern England. Part 3: Flora of the Bournemouth Beds; the Boscombe and the Highcliffe Sands.* Brit. Mus. nat. Hist., London, v, 169pp, 25 pl.

Cifelli, R. 1959. Bathonian Foraminifera of England. *Bull. compar. Zool., Harvard* **121**, 264–368.

Cleevely, R.J., Morris, N.J. and Bate, G. 1984. An ecological consideration and comparison of the Punfield Marine Band (Lower Aptian) Mollusca. *Proc. Dorset nat. Hist. archaeol. Soc.* **105** (for 1983), 93–106.

Clements, R.G. 1966. Some notes on the Purbeck Beds. *Proc. Dorset nat. Hist. archaeol. Soc.* **88**, 43–44.

Clements, R.G. 1969. Annotated cumulative section of the Purbeck beds between Peveril Point and the Zig-Zag Path, Durlston Bay. *In* Torrens, H.S. (Ed.), *International Field Symposium on the British Jurassic, Excursion No. 1, Guide for Dorset and South Somerset. Univ. Keele*, A35.

Clements, R.G. 1993. Type section of the Purbeck Limestone Group, Durlston Bay, Swanage, Dorset. *Proc. Dorset nat. Hist. archaeol. Soc.* **114** (for 1992) 181–206.

Collinson, M.E. 1983. Fossil Plants of the London Clay. *Palaeont. Assoc., Field Guides to Fossils No.1*, 121pp.

Colter, V.S. and Havard, D.J. 1981. The Wytch Farm Oil Field, Dorset. *In*, Illing, L.V. and Hobson, G.D. (eds.), *Petroleum geology of the continental shelf of North-West Europe.* Heyden & Son Ltd. 494–503.

Cope, J.C.W. 1967. The palaeontology and stratigraphy of the lower part of the Upper Kimmeridge Clay of Dorset. *Bull. Brit. Mus. nat. hist, (Geol.)* **15**, 1–79, 33 pl.

Cope, J.C.W. 1970–1979. Geology. *Proc. Dorset nat. Hist. archaeol. Soc.* **92** (1971 for 1970), 41–44; **93** (1972 for 1971), 38–40; **94** (1973 for 1972), 10; **95** (1974 for 1973), 105,6; **96** (1975 for 1974), 74; 97 (1976 for 1975), 70; **98** (1978 for 1976), 113; **100** (1980 for 1978), 130,1; **101** (1981 for 1979), 147.

Cope, J.C.W. 1978. The ammonite faunas and stratigraphy of the upper part of the Upper Kimmeridge Clay of Dorset. *Palaeontology* **21**, 469–533.

Cope, J.C.W., Duff, K.L., Parsons, C.F., Torrens, H.S., Wimbledon, W.A. and Wright, J.K. 1980. A Correlation of Jurassic Rocks of the British Isles. Part 2. *Geol. Soc. of Lond., Spec. Rept.* **15**, 109pp.

Cope, J.C.W., Getty, T.A., Howarth, M.K., Morton, N. and Torrens, H.S. 1980. A correlation of Jurassic Rocks of the British Isles. Part 1. *Geol. Soc. Lond., Spec. Rep.* **14**, 73pp.

Cosgrove, M.E. and Hearn, E.W. 1966. Structures in the Upper Purbeck Beds at Peveril Point, Swanage, Dorset. *Geol. Mag.* **103**, 498–507.

Cox, B.M. and Gallois, R.W. 1981. The stratigraphy of the Kimmeridge Clay of the Dorset type area and its correlation with some other Kimmeridgian sequences. *Rept Inst. geol. Sci.* **80/4**, 44pp.

Curry, D. 1976. The age of the Hengistbury Beds (Eocene) and its significance for the structure of the area around Christchurch, Dorset. *Proc. Geol. Ass.* **87**, 401–407.

Curry, D., Adams, C.G., Boulter, M.C., Dilley, F.C., Eames, F.E., Funnell, B.M. and Wells, M.K. 1978. A correlation of Tertiary rocks in the British Isles. *Geol. Soc. Lond., Spec. Rept.* **12**, 72pp.

Damon, R. 1884. *Geology of Weymouth, Portland, and the coast of Dorsetshire, from Swanage to Bridport-on-the-Sea : with natural history and archaeological notes. New & enlarged edition.* E. Stanford, London. xii, 250pp.

Davies, D.K. 1967. Origin of friable sandstone-calcareous sandstone rhythms in the Upper Lias of England. *Jl sedim. Petrol.* **37**, 1179−1188.

Davies, G.M. 1935. *The Dorset Coast, a Geological Guide*. Murby & Co., London. 126pp.

Davies, G.M. 1956. *The Dorset Coast, a Geological Guide*. A & C Black, London, 128pp.

Davies, K.H. and Keen, D.H. 1985. The age of Pleistocene marine deposits at Portland, Dorset. *Proc. Geol. Ass.* **96**, 217;1225.

Delair, J.B. 1958−1960. The Mesozoic Reptiles of Dorset. *Proc. Dorset nat. Hist. archaeol. Soc. Part 1*, **79** (1958 for 1957), 47−72: Part 2, **80** (1959 for 1958), 52−90: Part 3, **81** (1960 for 1959), 59−85.

Delair, J.B. 1962. Notes on Purbeck fossil footprints, with descriptions of two hitherto unknown from Dorset. *Proc. Dorset nat. Hist. archaeol. Soc.* **84** (for 1961), 92−100.

Delair, J.B. 1982. Multiple dinosaur trackways from the Isle of Purbeck. *Proc. Dorset nat. Hist. archaeol. Soc.* **102** (for 1980), 65−67.

Delair, J.B. 1986. Some little known Jurassic ichthyosaurs from Dorset. *Dorset. nat. Hist. archaeol. Soc.* **107** (for 1985), 127−134.

Dingwall, R.G. and Lott, G.K. 1979. IGS boreholes drilled from MV Whitehorn in the English Channel 1973−75. *Rept Inst. Geol. Sci. U.K.* **79/8**, ii, 45pp.

Donovan, D.T., and Stride, A.H. 1961. An acoustic survey of the sea floor south of Dorset and its geological interpretation. *Phil. Trans. R. Soc., Lond.* B **244**, 299−330, pl. 15−18.

Doornkamp, J.C. 1964. Subaerial landform development in relation to past sea levels in a part of south Dorset. *Proc. Dorset nat. Hist. archaeol. Soc.* **85** (for 1963), 71−77.

Douglas, J.A. and Arkell, W.J. 1928. The stratigraphical distribution of the Cornbrash: I. The South-Western Area. *Q. Jl. geol. Soc. Lond.* **84**, 117−178, pl. 9−12.

Downie, C. 1955. *The nature and origin of the Kimmeridge Oil Shale*. Ph.D. Thesis, University of Sheffield.

Downie, C. 1956. Mikroplankton from the Kimmeridge Clay. *Quart. Jl geol. Soc. Lond.* 112, 413−434, 1 pl.

Dru-Drury, G. 1949. The use of Purbeck Marble in Mediaeval times. *Proc. Dorset nat. Hist. archaeol. Soc.* **70** (for 1948), 74−98, pl. 7−35.

Drummond, P.V.O. 1970. The mid-Dorset Swell. Evidence of Albian-Cenomanian movements in Wessex. *Proc. Geol. Ass.* **81**, 679−714.

Dunn, C.E., 1974. Identification of sedimentary cycles through Fourier analysis of geochemical data. *Chem. Geol.* **13**, 217−232.

Dyer, K.R. 1975. The buried channels of the 'Solent River', southern England. *Proc. Geol. Ass.* **86**, 239−245.

Ebukanson, E.J. and Kinghorn, R.R.F. 1986. Oil and gas accumulations and their possible source rocks in southern England. *Jl Petroleum Geol.* **9**, 413−428.

Edmonds, J.M. 1978. The fossil collections of the Misses Philpot of Lyme Regis. *Proc. Dorset nat. Hist. archaeol. Soc.* **98** (for 1976), 43−53.

El-Shahat, A. and West, I. 1983. Early and late lithification of aragonitic bivalve beds in the Purbeck Formation (Upper Jurassic-Lower Cretaceous), of southern England. *Sediment. Geol.* **35**, 15−41.

Ensom, P.C. 1982. Geology in 1981. *Proc. Dorset nat. Hist. archaeol. Soc.* **103** (for 1981), 141.

Ensom, P.C. 1983. Geology in 1982. *Proc. Dorset nat. Hist. archaeol. Soc.* **104** (for 1982), 201,2.

Ensom, P.C. 1984a. Geology in 1983. *Proc. Dorset. nat. Hist. archaeol. Soc.* **105** (for 1983), 165−169.

Ensom, P.C. 1984b. A temporary exposure in the Purbeck Limestone Formation (Upper Purbeck Beds) at Friar Waddon Pumping Station, Dorset. *Proc. Dorset nat. Hist. archaeol. Soc.* **105** (for 1983), 89−91.

Ensom, P.C. 1985a. An annotated section of the Purbeck Limestone Formation at Worbarrow Tout, Dorset. *Proc. Dorset nat. Hist. archaeol. Soc.* **106** (for 1984), 87−91.

Ensom, P.C. 1985b. Geology Report. *Proc. Dorset nat. Hist. archaeol. Soc.* **106** (for 1984), 161–172.

Everard, C.E., 1956. Erosion platforms on the borders of the Hampshire basin. *Trans. Pap. Inst. Br. Geogr.* **22**, 33–46.

Falcon, N.L. and Kent, P.E. 1960. Geological results of petroleum exploration in Britain, 1945–1957. *Geol. Soc. Lond., Mem.* **2**, 56pp, 5 pl., 5 tables.

Farrimond, P., Comet, P., Eglinton, G., Evershed, R.P., Hall, M.A., Park, D.W. and Wardroper, A.M.K. 1984. Organic geochemical study of the Upper Kimmeridge Clay of the Dorset Type area. *Marine and Petroleum Geology* **1**, 340–354.

Fisher, O. 1856. On the Purbeck strata of Dorsetshire. *Trans. Cambridge phil. Soc.* **9**, 555–581.

Fowler, J. 1957. The geology of the Thornford pipe-trench. *Proc. Dorset nat. Hist. archaeol. Soc.* **78** (for 1956), 51–57.

Francis, J.E. 1983. The dominant conifer of the Jurassic Purbeck Formation, England. *Palaeontology* **26**, 277–294.

Fürsich, F.T. 1975. Trace fossils as environmental indicators in the Corallian of England and Normandy. Lethaia, **8**, 151–172.

Fürsich, F.T. 1976. Fauna-substrate relationships in the Corallian of England and Normandy. Lethaia, **9**, 343-356.

Fürsich, F.T. 1977. Corallian (Upper Jurassic) marine benthic associations from England and Normandy. *Palaeontology* **20**, 337–385.

Gallois, R.W. 1976. Coccolith blooms in the Kimmeridge Clay and origin of North Sea Oil. *Nature, London* **259**, 473–475.

Gardner, J.S. 1879. Description and correlation of the Bournemouth Beds.- Part I. Upper Marine Series. *Q. Jl geol. Soc., Lond.* **35**, 209–228.

Gardner, J.S. 1882. Description and correlation of the Bournemouth Beds. Part II. Lower or Freshwater Series. *Q. Jl geol. Soc., Lond.* **38**, 1–15.

Gatrall, M., Jenkyns, H.C. and Parsons, C.F. 1972. Limonitic concretions from the European Jurassic, with particular reference to the "snuff boxes" of southern England. *Sedimentology* **18**, 79–103.

Gibbs, A.D. 1984. Structural evolution of extensional basin margins. *Jl geol. Soc. Lond.* **141**, 609–620.

Gibbs, P. 1982. Observations of short term profile changes on Chesil Beach. *Dorset nat. Hist. archaeol. Soc.* **102** (for 1980), 77–82.

Goldring, R. and Stephenson, D.G. 1972. The depositional environment of three starfish beds. *N. Jb. Geol. Paläont., Mh.,* **H 10**, 611–624.

Grainger, P., Tubb, C.D.N., and Neilson, A.P.M. 1985. Landslide activity at the Pinhay water source, Lyme Regis. *Proc. Ussher Soc.* **6**, 246–252.

Green, J.F.N. 1946. The terraces of Bournemouth, Hants. *Proc. Geol. Ass.* **57**, 82–101, 1 pl.

Green, J.F.K. 1947. Some gravels and gravel pits in Hampshire and Dorset. *Proc. Geol. Ass.* **58**, 128–143.

Hallam, A. 1960. A sedimentary and faunal study of the Blue Lias of Dorset and Glamorgan. *Phil. Trans. R. Soc. Lond.* **B 243**, 1–44, pl. 1, 2.

Hallam, A. 1964. Origin of the limestone-shale rhythms in the Blue Lias of England: a composite theory. *J. Geol.* **72**, 157–169.

Hallam, A. 1967. An environmental study of the Upper Domerian and Lower Toarcian in Great Britain. *Phil. Trans. R. Soc. Lond.* **B 252**, 393–445, pl. 20.

Hallam, A. 1969. Tectonism and eustacy in the Jurassic. *Earth Sci. Rev.* **5**, 45–68.

Hallam, A. 1970. *Gyrochorte* and other trace fossils in the Forest Marble (Bathonian) of Dorset, England. *In* Crimes, T.P. and Harper, J.C. (eds.), *Trace Fossils.* Geol. Journal Special Issue No.3. Seel House Press, Liverpool, 189–200.

Hallam, A. 1975. *Jurassic Environments.* Cambridge University Press, Cambridge. 269pp.

Hallam, A. 1978. Eustatic cycles in the Jurassic. *Palaeogeography, Palaeoclimatol., Palaeoecol.* **23**, 1–32.

Hallam, A. 1981. A revised sea-level curve for the early Jurassic. *Jl geol. Soc. Lond.* **138**, 735–743.

Hallam, A. 1989. W.D. Lang's research on the Lias of Dorset. *Proc. geol. Ass.* **100**, 451–455.

Hancock, J.M. 1963. Upper Cretaceous. *Proc. Dorset nat. Hist. archaeol. Soc.* **84** (for 1962), 87.

Hancock, J.M. 1969. Transgression of the Cretaceous sea in South-west England. *Proc. Ussher Soc.* **2**, 61–83.

Handlirsch, A. 1906–8. *Die Fossilen insecten und die Phylogenie deʀ Rezenten Formen. Jurassic* **1**. Leipzig, 411–660.

Harris, T.M. 1939. *British Purbeck Charophyta.* Brit. Museum (Nat. Hist.), 83pp, 17 pl.

Haslett, S.K. 1992. Rhaxellid sponge microscleres from the Portlandian of Dorset, UK. *Geol. Jl* **27**, 239–347.

Heap, W., 1957. The Mammal Bed of Durlston Bay. *Dorset Year Book 1957–1958*, p. 83–85.

Hollingworth, S.E. 1938. The Purbeck Broken Beds. *Geol. Mag.* **75**, 330–332.

Holloway, S. 1983. The shell-detrital calcirudites of the Forest Marble Formation (Bathonian) of southwest England. *Proc. Geol. Ass.* **94**, 259–266.

Hooker, J.J. 1975. Report of Field Meeting to Hengistbury Head and adjacent areas, Dorset ; with an account of published work and some new exposures. *Tertiary Times* **2**, 109–121.

Hooker, J.J. 1977. The Creechbarrow limestone - its biota and correlation. *Tertiary Res.* **1**, 139–145.

Hooker, J.J. 1986. Mammals from the Bartonian (middle/late Eocene) of the Hampshire Basin, southern England. *Bull. Br. Mus. (nat. Hist.) Geol.* **39**, 191–478.

Hooker, J.J. and Insole, A.N. 1980. The distribution of mammals in the English Palaeogene. *Tertiary Res.* **3**, 31–45.

Hounsell, S.S.B. 1952. Portland and its Stone. *Mine and Quarry Engineering* **18**, 107–114.

Hounsell, S.S.B. 1962. The quarrying of Portland Stone. *The Quarry Manager's Journal, 1962*, 1–8 (of reprint).

House, M.R. 1955. New records of the Red Nodule beds near Weymouth. *Proc. Dorset nat. Hist. archaeol. Soc.* **75**, 134–5.

House, M.R. 1957. The Fuller's Earth outcrop in South Dorset. *Proc. Dorset nat. Hist. arch. Soc.* **78** (for 1956), 64–70.

House, M.R. 1958. The Dorset Coast from Poole to the Chesil Beach. *Geologists' Association Guides* **22**, 21pp.

House, M.R. 1961. The structure of the Weymouth Anticline. *Proc. Geol. Ass.* **71**, 221–238.

House, M.R. 1963. Dorset Geology, 1950–1960. *Proc. Dorset nat. Hist. archaeol. Soc.* **84** (for 1962), 77–91.

House, M.R. 1963–1970. Geology. Proc. Dorset. nat. Hist. archaeol. Soc. **84** (1963 for 1962), 36; **85** (1964 for 1963), 38,9; **86** (1965 for 1964), 38–40; **87** (1966 for 1965), 4–5; **88** (1967 for 1966), 41; **89** (1968 for 1967), 41–45; **90** (1969 for 1968), 43, 44; **91** (1970 for 1969), 38,39.

House, M.R. 1969. The Dorset coast from Poole to the Chesil Beach. 2nd Edition, Geologists' Association Guides **22**, 32pp.

House, M.R. 1970. Portland Stone on Portland. *Proc. Dorset nat. Hist. archaeol. Soc.* **91** (for 1969), 38,39.

House, M.R. 1974. The Sutton Poyntz, Poxwell and Chaldon Herring Anticlines; a reinterpretation. *Proc. Geol. Ass.* **84**, 477,8.

House, M.R. 1985. A new approach to an absolute timescale from measurements of orbital cycles and sedimentary microrhythms. *Nature, London* **315**, 721–725.

House, M.R. 1987. Are Jurassic sedimentary microrhythms due to orbital forcing? *Proc. Ussher Soc.* **6**, 299–311.

House, M.R. 1992. Dorset Dolines : Part 2, Bronkham Hill. *Proc. Dorset nat. Hist. archaeol. Soc.* **113** (for 1991), 149–155.

Howarth, M.K. 1957. The Middle Lias of the Dorset coast. *Q. Jl geol. Soc. Lond.* **113**, 185–204.

Howarth, M.K. 1980. The Toarcian age of the upper part of the Marlstone Rock Bed of England. *Palaeontology* **23**, 637–656.

Ioannides, N.S., Stavrinos, G.N. and Downie, C. 1976. Kimmeridgian microplankton from Clavell's Hard, Dorset, England. *Micropaleontology* **22**, 443–478.

Institute of Geological Sciences. 1983. IGS Borehole 1981. *Rept. Inst. geol. Sci.* **82/11**, 1–3.

Irwin, H. 1979. On an environmental model for the type Kimmeridge Clay. *Nature, London* **279**, 819.

Irwin, H. 1980. Early diagenetic carbonate precipitation and pore fluid migration in the Kimmeridge Clay of Dorset, England. *Sedimentology* **27**, 577–591.

Jackson, J.F. 1922. Appendix 1. Sections of the Junction-Bed and contiguous deposits. *Q. Jl geol. Soc. Lond.* **78**, 436–448.

Jackson, J.F. 1926. The Junction-Bed of the Middle and Upper Lias on the Dorset coast. *Q. Jl geol. Soc. Lond.* **82**, 490–525, 2 pl.

Jarvis, I. and Tocher, B.A. 1987. Field Meeting: the Cretaceous of SE Devon, 14-16th March, 1986. *Proc. Geol. Ass.* **98**, 51–66.

Jarzembowski, E. 1991. The fossil dragonflies of Dorset. *In*: Prendergast, E.D.V. *The dragonflies of Dorset*. Dorset Nat. Hist. & Archaeol. Soc., 59–62.

Jarzembowski, E. 1993. A provisional checklist of fossil insects from the Purbeck Beds of Dorset. *Proc. Dorset nat. Hist. archaeol. Soc.* **114** (for 1992) 174–179.

Jenkyns, H.C. and Senior, J.R. 1977. A liassic palaeofault from Dorset. *Geol. Mag.* **114**, 47–52.

Jenkyns H.C. and Senior, J.R. 1991. Geological evidence for intra-Jurassic faulting in the Wessex Basin and its margins. *Jl geol. Soc. London* **148**, 245–260.

Jones, D.K.C. (Ed.), 1980. *The shaping of southern England. Inst. Br. Geogr., Spec. Publ.* **11**, Academic press. 274pp.

Jones, M.E., Allison, R.J. and Gilligan, J. 1984. On the relationship between geology and coastal landform in central southern England. *Proc. Dorset nat. Hist. archaeol. Soc.* **105** (for 1983), 107-118.

Kelly, S.R.A. 1988. *Laevitrigonia cineris* sp. nov., a bivalve from near the Jurassic-Cretaceous Boundary in the Durlston formation (Purbeck Limestone Group) of Dorset. *Proc. Dorset nat. Hist. archaeol. Soc.* **109** (for 1987), 112–116.

Kennedy, W.J. 1970. A correlation of the uppermost Albian and Cenomanian of south-west England. *Proc. Geol. Ass.* **81**, 613–677.

Kennedy, W.J. 1971. Cenomanian ammonites from southern England. *Spec. Pap. Palaeontol.* **8**, 133pp, 64 pl.

Lake, S.D. 1986a. Evidence for Bathonian and Portlandian synsedimentary fault movements in Dorset. *Proc. Dorset nat. Hist. archaeol. Soc.* **107** (for 1985), 189–190.

Lake, S.D. 1986b. Brecciated pipes in the Broken Beds, Purbeck Limestone Formation. *Proc. Dorset nat. Hist. archaeol. Soc.* **107** (for 1985), 191–192.

Lake, S.D. and Karner, G.D. 1987. The structure and evolution of the Wessex Basin, southern England: an example of inversion tectonics. *Tectonophysics* **137**, 347–378.

Lang, W.D. 1924. The Blue Lias of the Devon and Dorset coasts. *Proc. Geol. Ass.* **35**, 169–185, 1 pl.

Lang, W.D. 1936. The Green Ammonite Beds of the Dorset Lias. *Q. Jl geol. Soc. Lond.* **92**, 423–437, 1 pl.

Lang, W.D. 1939. Mary Anning and the pioneer geologists of Lyme. *Proc. Dorset nat. Hist. archaeol. Soc.* **60**, 142–164, pl. 25–128.

Lang, W.D. 1956. Mary Anning and Anna Maria Pinney. *Proc. Dorset nat. Hist. arch. Soc.* **76** (for 1954), 146–152.

Lang, W.D. 1956–1959. Geology. *Proc. Dorset nat. Hist. archaeol. Soc.* **76** (1956 for 1954), 110; **77** (1956 for 1955), 39,40; **78** (1957 for 1956), 30–31; **79** (1958 for 1957), 23–25; **80** (1959 for 1958), 22.

Lang, W.D. 1961. Submerged Forest. *Proc. Dorset nat. Hist. archaeol. Soc.* **82** (for 1960), 38–39.

Lang, W.D., Spath, L.F., with notes by Cox, L.R., Muir-Wood, H.M. Trueman, A.E. and Williams, D.M. 1926. The Black Marl of Black Ven and Stonebarrow, in the Lias of the Dorset coast. *Q. Jl geol. Soc. Lond.* **82**, 144–187, pl. 8–11.

Lang, W.D., Spath, L.F., Cox, L.R. and Muir-Wood, H.M. 1928. The Belemnite Marls of Charmouth, a series in the Lias of the Dorset coast. *Q. Jl geol. Soc. Lond.* **84**, 179–257, pl. 13–18.

Lang, W.D., Spath, L.F. and Richardson, W.A. 1923. Shales-with-'Beef', a sequence in the Lower Lias of the Dorset coast. *Q. Jl geol. Soc. London* **79**, 47–99.

Leddra, M.J., Yassir, N.A., Jones, C. and Jones, M.E. 1987. Anomalous compressional structures formed during diagenesis of a dolostone at Kimmeridge Bay, Dorset. *Proc. Geol. Ass.* **98**, 145–155.

Lord, A.R. and Bown, P.R. (Eds.) 1987. Mesozoic and Cenozoic stratigraphical micropalaeontology of the Dorset Coast and Isle of Wight, Southern England. *British Micropalaeontol. Soc., Guidebook* **1**, 183pp.

Macfadyen, W.A. 1970. *Geological highlights of the West Country.* Butterworth & Co. Ltd., London. 296pp.

Melville, R.V. and Freshney, E.C. 1982. *The Hampshire Basin and adjoining areas.* Inst. Geol. Sci., H.M.S.O., 146pp.

Miles, J.A., Downes, C.J. and Cook, S.E. 1993. The fossil oil seep in Mupe Bay, Dorset : a myth invesstigated. *Mar. Petrol. Geol.* **10**, 58–70.

Mitchell, G.F., Penny, L.F., Shotton, F.W. and West, R.G. 1973. A correlation of Quaternary deposits in the British Isles. *Geol. Soc. Lond., Spec. Rept.* **4**, 99pp.

Morris, K.A. 1979. A classification of Jurassic marine shale sequences: an example from the Toarcian (Lower Jurassic) of Great Britain. *Palaeogeogr., Palaeoclimatol. Palaeoecol.* **26**, 117–126.

Morter, A.A. 1984. Purbeck-Wealden Beds Mollusca and their relationship to ostracod biostratigraphy, stratigraphical correlation and palaeoecology in the Weald and adjacent areas. *Proc. Geol. Ass.* **95**, 217–234.

Mortimore, R.N. and Pomerol, B. 1987. Correlation of the Upper Cretaceous White Chalk (Turonian to Campanian) in the Anglo-Paris Basin. *Proc. Geol. Ass.* **98**, 97–143.

Mottram, B.H. 1950. Notes on the structure of the Poxwell Pericline, and the Ridgeway Fault at Bincombe Tunnel, Dorset. *Proc. Dorset nat. Hist. archaeol. Soc.* **71** (for 1949), p.175–183.

Mottram, B.H. and House, M.R. 1956. The structure of the northern margin of the Poxwell Pericline. *Proc. Dorset nat. Hist. archaeol. Soc.* **76** (for 1954), p.129–135.

Muir-Wood, H.M. 1936a. Brachiopoda from the Lower Lias, Green Ammonite Beds, of Dorset. *Q. Jl geol. Soc. Lond.* **92**, 472–487.

Muir-Wood, H.M. 1936. Monograph on the brachiopoda of the British Great Oolite series, Part I, The Brachiopoda of the Fuller's Earth. *Monogr. Palaeontogr. Soc.* **404**, p. ii + 144, pl.1–5.

Nunn, J.F. 1992. A geological map of Purbeck Beds in the northern part of Durlston Bay. *Proc. Dorset nat. Hist. archaeol. Soc.* **113** (for 1991), 145–148.

Oldham, T.C.B. Flora of the Wealden plant debris beds England. *Palaeontology* **19**, 437–502.

Oschmann, W. 1988. Kimmeridge Clay sedimentation a new cyclic model. *Palaeogeogr., Palaeoclimatol., Palaeoecol.* **65**, 217–251.

Page, K.N. 1992. The sequence of ammonite correlated horizons in the British Sinemurian (Lower Jurassic). *Newsl. Strat.* **27**, 129–156.

Palmer, C.P. 1966. The fauna of Day's Shell Bed in the Middle Lias of the Dorset coast. *Proc. Dorset nat. Hist. archaeol. Soc.* **87** (for 1965), 69–80.

Palmer, C.P. 1972. Revision of the zonal classification of the Lower Lias of the Dorset coast. *Proc. Dorset nat. Hist archaeol Soc.* **93** (for 1963), 102–116.

Palmer, S.L. 1964. Prehistoric stone industries of the Fleet area, Weymouth. *Proc. Dorset nat. Hist. archaeol. Soc.* **85** (for 1963), 107–115.

Palmer, T.J. and Wilson, M.A. 1990. Growth of ferruginous oncoliths in the Bajocian (Middle Jurassic) of Europe. *Terra Nova* **2**, 142–147.

Parsons, C.F. 1975. The stratigraphy of the Stony Head Cutting. *Proc. Dorset nat. Hist. & Arch. Soc.* **96** (for 1974), 8–13.

Penn, I.E., Chadwick, R.A., Holloway, S., Roberts, G., Pharaoh, T.C., Allsop, J.M., Hulbert, A.G. and Burns, I.M. 1987. Principal features of the hydrocarbon prospectivity of the Wessex-Channel Basin, U.K. In: *Petroleum geology of N.W. Europe*, Vol. 1 (Ed. Brooks, J. and Glennie, K.W.). Graham and Trotman, London, p. 109–118.

Penn, I.E., Dingwall, R.G. and Knox, R.W. O'B. Knox. 1980. The Inferior Oolite (Bajocian) sequence from a borehole in Lyme Bay, Dorset. *Rept. Inst. geol. Sci.* **79/3**, 27pp.

Penn, I.E., Merriman, R.J. and Wyatt, R.J. 1979. The Bathonian strata of the Bath-Frome area. *Rept. Inst. geol. Sci.* **78/22**, 88pp.

Phillips, W.J. 1964. The structures in the Jurassic and Cretaceous rocks on the Dorset coast between White Nothe and Mupe Bay. *Proc. Geol. Ass.* **75**, 373–405.

Pitts, J. 1982. An historical survey of the landslips of the Axmouth-Lyme Regis undercliff, S. Devon. *Proc. Dorset nat. Hist. archaeol. Soc.* **103** (for 1981), 101–106.

Pitts, J. 1984. The recent evolution of landsliding in the Axmouth-Lyme Regis Undercliffs National Nature Reserve. *Proc. Dorset nat. Hist. archaeol. Soc.* **105** (for 1983), 119–125.

Plint, A.G. 1982. Eocene sedimentation and tectonics in the Hampshire Basin. *Jl geol. Soc. Lond.* **139**, 249–254.

Preece, R.C. 1980. The Mollusca of the Creechbarrow Limestone Formation (Eocene) of Creechbarrow Hill, Dorset. *Tertiary Res.* **2**, 169–184.

Pugh, M.E. 1968. Algae from the Lower Purbeck Limestones of Dorset. *Proc. Geol. Ass.* **79**, 513–523, pl 13–18.

Pugh, M.E. and Shearman, D.J. 1967. Cryoturbation structures at the south end of the Isle of Portland. *Proc. Geol. Ass.* **78**, 463–471.

Radley, J.D. 1986. Notes on a Bajocian stromatolitic limestone from Burton Bradstock, Dorset. *Proc. Dorset. nat. Hist. archaeol. Soc.* **107**, 184–186.

Ramsay, J.G. 1991. Some geometric problems of ramp-flat thrust models. *In*: McClay, K.R. (ed). *Thrust tectonics*, Chapman & Hall, 191–200.

Rawson, P.F., Curry, D., Dilley, F.C., Hancock, J.M., Kennedy, W.J., Neale, J.W., Wood C.J. and Worssam, B.C. 1978. A correlation of Cretaceous rocks in the British Isles. *Geol. Soc. Lond., Spec. Rept.* **9**, 70pp.

Reid, C. 1896. The Eocene deposits of Dorset. *Q. Jl geol. Soc. London* **52**, 490–496.

Reid, C. 1899. *The Geology of the country around Dorchester.* Mem. geol. Surv. Engl. & Wales, Sheet 328, 52pp.

Rhys, G.H., Lott, G.K. and Calver, M.A. (Eds). 1982. The Winterborne Kingston borehole, Dorset, England. *Rept. Inst. geol. Sci.* **81/3**, 196pp.

Richardson, L. 1909. The Dorset and Hampshire coasts with particular reference to the Forest Marble beds near Langton Herring. *Proc. Cotteswold nat. Field Club* **16**, 267–272.

Richardson, L. 1928–1930. The Inferior Oolite and contiguous deposits of the Burton Bradstock-Broadwindsor district, Dorset. *Proc. Cotteswold Nat. Fld Club* **23**, 35–68; 149–185; 253–264, pl. 2–6, 19–25, 28.

Ridd, M.F. 1973. The Sutton Poyntz, Poxwell and Chaldon Herring anticlines, southern England: a reinterpretation. *Proc. Geol. Ass.* **84**, 1–8.

Robbie, J.A. 1950. The Chalk Rock at Winterbourne Abbas, Dorset. *Geol. Mag.* **87**, 209–213.

Rowe, A.W. 1901. The zones of the White Chalk of the English coast. Part II, Dorset. *Proc. Geol. Ass.* **17**, 1–76, pl. 1–10.

Rowe, A.W. 1903. The zones of the White Chalk of the English coast. Part III, Devon. *Proc. Geol. Ass.* **18**, 1–51, pl. 1–13.

Ruffell, A.H. 1992. The Lower Greensand Group (Aptian–Albian) at Swanage : correlation with the Isle of Wight type section. *Proc. Ussher Soc.* **8**, 74–76.

Sandy, M.R. 1985a. Sedimentary microrhythms. *Nature, London* **318**, 81.

154   M. R. HOUSE

Sandy, M.R. 1985b. Brachiopods from the Jurassic Abbotsbury Ironstone, Abbotsbury. *Proc. Dorset nat. Hist. archaeol. Soc.* **106** (for 1984), 171–2.

Sellwood, B.W. 1970. The relation of trace fossils to small-scale sedimentary cycles in the British Lias. *In*: Crimes, T.P. and Harper, J.C. (eds.). *Trace Fossils*, Geol. Journal Spec. Issue No.3, Seel House Press, Liverpool, 489–584.

Sellwood, B.W. 1972. Regional environmental changes across a Lower Jurassic stage-boundary in Britain. *Palaeontology*, 15, 125–157.

Sellwood, B.W., Durkin, M.K. and Kennedy, W.J. 1970. Field meeting on the Jurassic and Cretaceous rocks of Wessex. *Proc. Geol. Ass.* **81**, 715–732.

Sellwood, B.W. and Jenkyns, H.C. 1975. Basins and swells and the evolution of an epeiric sea (Pliensbachian-Bajocian of Great Britain). *Jl. Geol. Soc. Lond.* **131**, 373–388.

Sellwood, B.W., Scott, J. and Lunn, G. 1986. Mesozoic basin evolution in southern England. *Proc. Geol. Ass.* **97**, 259–289.

Sellwood, B.W. and Wilson, R.C.L. 1990. *Jurassic Sedimentary environments of the Wessex Basin.* 13th International Sedimentological Congress, Nottingham, UK. 1990. Field Guide No. 7. 89pp.

Senior, J.R., Parsons, C.F., and Torrens, H.S. 1970. New sections in the Inferior Oolite of South Dorset. *Proc. Dorset nat. Hist. archaeol. Soc.* **91** (for 1969), 114–119.

Simpson, M.I. 1983. Decapod Crustacea and associated fauna of the Punfield Marine Band (Lower Cretaceous: Lower Aptian), Punfield, Dorset. *Proc. Dorset Nat. Hist. archaeol. Soc.* **104** (for 1982), 143–146.

Simms, M.J. 1986. Contrasting lifestyles in Lower Jurassic crinoids: a comparison of benthic and pseudopelagic Isocrinida. *Palaeontology* 29, 475–493.

Smith, A.B. (Ed.) 1987. Fossils of the Chalk. Palaeont. Ass., *Field Guides to Fossils No.2*, 306pp.

Sparks, B.W. 1951. Two drainage diversions in Dorset. *Geography* **36**, 186–193.

Sparks, B.W. 1953. Stages in the physical evolution of the Weymouth lowland. *Trans. Pap. Inst. Br. Geogr.* **18** (for 1953), 17–29.

Sperling, C.H.B., Goudie, A.S., Stoddart, D.R. and Poole, G.G. 1977. Dolines in the Dorset chalklands and other areas in southern Britain. *Trans. Inst. Br. Geogr., N.S.* **2**, 205–223.

Stoneley, R. 1982. The structural development of the Wessex Basin. *Jl geol. Soc. Lond.* **139**, 543–554.

Stoneley, R. and Selley, R.C. 1986. *A field guide to the petroleum geology of the Wessex Basin.* R.C. Selley & Co. Ltd. 43pp.

Strahan, A. 1898. *The Geology of the Isle of Purbeck and Weymouth.* Mem. geol. Surv. Engl. & Wales, xi, 278 pp. 11 pl.

Summerfield, M.A., 1979. Origin and palaeoenvironmental interpretation of sarsens. *Nature, London* **281**, 137–139.

Sun, S.Q. 1989. A new interpretation of the Corallian (Upper Jurassic) cycles of the Dorset coast, southern England. *Geol. Jl* 24, 139–158.

Sylvester-Bradley, P.C. 1948. Field meeting at Weymouth, Dorset. *Proc. Geol. Ass.* **59**, 141–150.

Sylvester-Bradley, P.C. 1949. The ostracod genus *Cypridea* and the zones of the Upper and Middle Purbeckian. *Proc. Geol. Ass.* **60**, 125–153.

Sylvester-Bradley, P.C. 1957. The Forest Marble of Dorset. *Proc. geol. Soc. Lond.* **1556**, 26–28.

Talbot, M.R. 1973. Major sedimentary cycles in the Corallian Beds (Oxfordian of southern England). *Palaeogeogr., Palaeoclimatol., Palaeoecol.* **14**, 293–317.

Talbot, M.R. 1974. Ironstones in the Upper Oxfordian of southern England. *Sedimentology* 21, 433–450.

Taylor, J.C.M. 1986. Gas prospects in the Variscan thrust province of southern England. *Geol. Soc., Lond., Spec. Publ.* **23**, 37–53.

Taylor, M.A. and Benton, M.J. 1986. Reptiles from the Upper Kimmeridge Clay

(Kimmeridgian, Upper Jurassic) of the vicinity of Egmont Bight, Dorset. *Proc. Dorset nat. Hist. archaeol. Soc.* **107** (for 1985), 121–125.

Thomas, J. and Ensom, P. 1989. *Bibliography and Index of Dorset Geology.* Dorset nat. Hist. archaeol. Soc. (in press).

Torrens, H.S. (ed.), 1969. *International Field Symposium on the British Jurassic, Excursion No.1, Guide for Dorset and South Somerset.* Univ. Keele. 71pp.

Townson, W.G. 1974. Geology of Coombe Valley. *Proc. Dorset nat. Hist. archaeol. Soc.* **95** (for 1973), 7,8.

Townson, W.G. 1975. Lithostratigraphy and deposition of the type Portlandian. *Jl. geol. Soc. Lond.* **131**, 619–638.

Tyson, R.V., Wilson, R.C.L. and Downie, C. 1979. A stratified water column environmental model for the type Kimmeridge Clay. *Nature, London* **277**, 377–380.

Walker, C.T. 1964. Depositional environment of Purbeck Formation. *Geol. Mag.,* **101**, 189–190.

Walter, B. 1967. Révision de la faune Bryozoaire du Bajocian Supérieur de Shipton Gorge. *Trav. Lab. géol., Fac. Sci. Lyon, NS,* **14**, 43–52.

Warrington, G., Audley-Charles, M.G., Elliott, R.E., Evans, W.B., Ivimey-Cook, H.C., Kent, P.E., Robinson, P.L., Shotton, F.W. and Taylor, F.M. 1980. A correlation of Triassic rocks in the British Isles. *Geol. Soc. Lond., Spec. Rept.* **13**, 78pp.

Warrington, G. and Scrivener, R.C. 1980. Lyme Regis (1901) Borehole succession and its relationship to the Triassic sequence of the east Devon coast. *Proc. Ussher Soc.* **5**, 24–32.

Waters, R.S. 1960. The bearing of superficial deposits on the age and origin of the upland plain of East Devon, West Dorset and South Somerset. *Trans. Pap. Inst. Brit. geogr.* **28**, 89–97.

Weedon, G.P. 1986. Hemipelagic shelf sedimentation and climatic cycles: the basal Jurassic (Blue Lias) of south Britain. *Earth and Planetary Science Letters,* **76**, 321–335.

West, I.M., 1960. On the occurrence of celestine in the Caps and Broken Beds at Durlston Head, Dorset. *Proc. Geol. Ass.,* **71**, 391–401.

West, I.M. 1975. Evaporite and associated sediments of the basal Purbeck Formation (Upper Jurassic) of Dorset. *Proc. Geol. Ass.* **86**, 205–225.

West, I.M. 1979. Review of evaporite diagenesis in the Purbeck Formation of southern England. In Sédimentation Jurassique W. Européen, *A.S.F. Publ. Spec., No.1,* 407–416.

West, I.M. and Hooper, M.J. 1969. Detrital Portland chert and limestone in the Upper Purbeck Beds at Friar Waddon, Dorset. *Geol. Mag.,* 106, 277–280.

West, I.M., Shearman, D.J. and Pugh, M.E. 1969. Whitsun Field Meeting in the Weymouth area, 1966. *Proc. Geol. Ass.* **80**, 331–340, 1 pl.

Whalley, P.E.S. 1985. The systematics and palaeogeography of the Lower Jurassic insects of Dorset, England. *Bull. Br. Mus. (nat. Hist.) Geol.* **39**, 107–189.

Wignall, P.B. and Ruffell, A.H. 1990. The influence of a sudden climatic change on marine deposition in the Kimmeridgian of North West Europe. *Jl geol. Soc. London* **147**, 365–371.

Williams, G.D. and Brooks, M. 1985. A reinterpretation of the concealed Variscan structure beneath southern England by section balancing. *Jl geol. Soc. Lond.* **142**, 689–695.

Williams, P.F.V. 1986. Petroleum geochemistry of the Kimmeridge Clay of onshore southern and eastern England. *Marine & Petroleum Geology* 3, 258–281.

Wilson, R.C.L. 1967. Diagenetic carbonate fabric variations in Jurassic limetones in southern England. *Proc. Geol. Ass.* **78**, 535–554.

Wilson, R.C.L. 1968. Carbonate facies variations within the Osmington Oolite Series in southern England. *Palaeogeogr., Palaeoclimatol., Palaeoecol.* **4**, 89–123.

Wilson, R.C.L. 1980. *Changing sea levels: a Jurassic case study. Science: A third level Course; Case Studies in Earth Science. Course S335.* The Open University Press. 120pp.

Wilson, V., Welch, F.B.A., Robbie, J.A. and Green, G.W. 1958. *Geology of the country around Bridport and Yeovil.* Mem. geol. Surv. G.B. xii, 239pp.

Wimbledon, W.A. 1987. Rhythmic sedimentation in the late Jurassic-early Cretaceous. *Proc. Dorset nat. Hist. archaeol. Soc.* **108** (for 1986), 127–133.

Wimbledon, W.A. and Cope, J.C.W. 1978. The ammonite faunas of the English Portland Beds and the zones of the Portlandian Stage. *Q. Jl geol. Soc. Lond.* **135**, p.183–190.

Wimbledon, W.A. and Hunt, C.O. 1983. The Portland-Purbeck junction (Portlandian-Berriasian) in the Weald, and correlation of latest Jurassic-early Cretaceous rocks in southern England. *Geol. Mag.* **120**, 267–280.

Woodward, A.S. 1916-1919. The Fossil Fishes of English Wealden and Purbeck Formations. *Monogr. Palaeontogr. Soc.* **334**, 1–48, pl. i-x, **336**, p 49–104, pl. xi-xx, **340**, p 105-148, pl. xxi-xxv.

Woodward, H.B. and Ussher, W.A.E. 1911. *Geology of the Country near Sidmouth and Lyme Regis.* 2nd Edition. Mem. geol. Surv. Engl. & Wales, Sheets 326 & 340.

Wright, J.K. 1986a. A new look at the stratigraphy, sedimentology and ammonite fauna of the Corallian Group (Oxfordian) of south Dorset. *Proc. Geol. Ass.* **97**, 1–21.

Wright, J.K. 1986b. The Upper Oxford Clay at Furzy Cliff, Dorset: stratigraphy, palaeoenvironment and ammonite fauna. *Proc. Geol. Ass.* **97**, 221–228.

Young, D. 1972. Brickmaking in Dorset. *Proc. Dorset nat. Hist. archaeol. Soc.* **93** (for 1971), 213–242.

Ziegler, B. 1962. Die Ammonitengattung in Oberjura (Taxionomie, Stratigraphie, Biologie). *Palaeontographica* **A119**, p.1–172.

Michael R. House
Department of Geology
The University of Southampton,
SOUTHAMPTON, S09 5NH.

INDEX

Aalenian, 14
Abbotsbury, 64–66
  Fault, 33, 35, 57, 62, 64, 88, 98
  Ironstone, Iron Ore, 5, 11, 41, 64
  Sandstone, 64
  Syncline, 64, 65
Acanthoceras, 17
Aculeata Zone, 16
Aegoceras, 54
Agglestone, Grit, 128, 130, 132
Albani Zone, 15
Albian Stage, 8, 17, 57, 125
Algae, 24, 106, 120
Alsatites, 13
Alum Chine, 139
Amaltheus, 13, 54–56
Amoeboceras, 15
Ammonoidea, ammonites, 13, 22
  dimorphism, 23, 54
  heteromorphs, 23
Anahoplites, 109, 125
Androgynoceras, 54
angiosperms, 24
Anguiformis Zone, 15
Angulata Zone, 13
Annelida, 21
Anning, Mary, 43
Apectodinium, 18
Apiocrinites, 21, 69
Apoderoceras, 44
Aptian Stage, 8, 11, 16
Aptyxiella, 22, 77
Arenicolites, 84
arenites, 27, 32
Arietites, 13
argillites, 27, 32
Arnioceras, 13, 53
artefacts, 10
Arthropoda, arthropods, 21
Asphinctites, 14
Aspidioides Zone, 14
Astarte, 55, 137
Asteroceras, 13, 53
Asterosoma, 81
asterozoans, 21
Athleta Zone, 14
Aulacostephanus, 15, 64, 92, 110, 113, 114

Autissiodorensis Zone, 15, 113
Avonothyris, 62, 69

Bagshot Beds, 5, 9, 11, 66
Bajocian, 14
Ballard Cliff, 125
Ballard Down, 4, 124–127
  Fault, 126, 127
Barton Clay, 133
Bathonian, 14
Bat's Head, 4, 34, 99, 102, 104
Baylei Zone, 15
Beaniceras, 54, 55
beef, 53, 122
Beer Head Limestone, 9, 17
Belemnella, 17
Belemnitella, 17
Belemnite Marls, 7, 13, 53–55
belemnites, 23
Belemnite Stone, 7, 13, 55
Bembridge Beds, 5
Bencliff Grit, 81, 82
benthos, 25
Berry Knap, 69
Bincombe, 9, 86, 87
  Railway Cutting, 86–88
Black Head, 78, 81, 83
  Siltstones, 82
Blackstone, 8, 64, 73, 85, 92, 111–115
Black Ven Marls, 7, 52, 53
Blue Lias, 6, 7, 13, 46, 50–53
Boreholes;
  Chaldon, 94, 96–98
  Chesil Beach, 39, 40
  Christchurch, 136, 140
  Cranborne, 1
  Lulworth, 99
  Lyme Regis, 1, 43, 44, 47–52
  Kimmeridge, 109–116
  Nettlecombe, 1
  Poxwell, 93–95
  Sea Barn Farm, 62, 67, 69
  Seaborough, 1
  West Bay, 62
  Winterborne Kingston, 1, 133
  Wytch Farm, 132–135

157

Plate 1

A. Pinhay Bay west of Lyme Regis. Massive limestones of the White Lias (Lilstock Formation) overlain by alternating limestones and shales of the Blue Lias with the base of the Shales with Beef at the top.

B. The base of the Jurassic is drawn where *Psiloceras* enters in the early Blue Lias, 2.5m above the base of the Blue Lias on the east side of Pinhay Bay. Tonya marks the level, Bed H25, with her hand.

Plate 2

A. Rhythmicity in the Blue Lias near Seven Rock Point. The sequence at the hammer shows black kerogen-rich paper shales followed by grey mudrock and then limestones.

B. A limestone in the Blue Lias showing the branching burrows of *Thalassinoides* and much finer, spaghetti-like burrows of *Chondrites*.

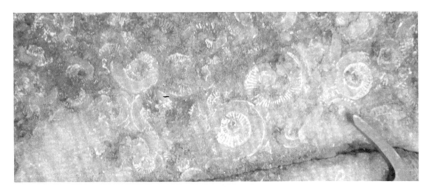

C. A limestone surface of the Blue Lias covered with crushed schlotheimiid ammonites.

Plate 3

A. The upper Blue Lias just east of Seven Rock Point. Top Quick and Venty (Beds 45 & 43) are at the top. The thick bed straddled by the two-metre scale is Specketty (Bed 19) just above which the Hettangian/Sinemurian boundary is drawn.

B. The cliffs east of Charmouth viewed from above Chippell Bay. Cretaceous yellow sands cap Stonebarrow (left) and Golden Cap (middle). The band of vertical pale-grey cliffs below Stonebarrow is the Belemnite Marls. The vertical cliffs in the extreme distance on the right are the Bridport Sands east of West Bay.

C. Telephoto view from Charmouth east to Golden Cap. The slipped cliffs in the foreground are the Shales with Beef. The vertical blue-grey marls above are the Belemnite Marls. The lowest bench of the cliff of Golden Cap is formed of the Pliensbachian Three Tiers with the Green Ammonite Beds below.

Plate 4

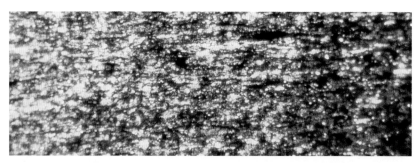

A. Thin section of black shales immediately above Specketty (Bed 19) of the Blue Lias showing lamination of organic debris and detrital grains. About ×30.

B. Surface at the Belemnite Stone (Bed 121), Pliensbachian, at sea level on the east side of Golden Cap.

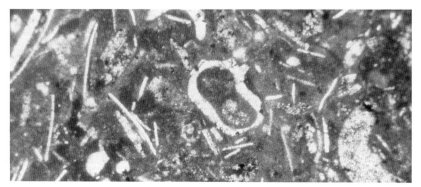

C. Thin section of the Marlstone Rock Band, top Pliensbachian and Middle Lias, from Eype Mouth, showing shell fragments set in a ferruginous calcilutite. About ×30.

Plate 5

A. Golden Cap from just east of Seatown. The Middle Lias Down Cliff Sands (Pliensbachian) are in the foreground. The profile of Gold Cap in the distance shows a lower vertical cliff of the Green Ammonite Beds with a ledge above formed of the Three Tiers which mark the base of the Middle Lias. The succeeding slope is of Eype Clay and Down Cliff Sands (also Middle Lias) capped by the transgressive yellow sands of the Cretaceous (Albian).

B,C. The profile of Thorncombe Beacon and Hope Corner; a telephoto taken from Burton Cliff. The yellow Thorncombe Sands (upper Middle Lias) from the top of the cliff to the right and the middle cliff below Thorncombe Beacon where they are overlain by Down Cliff Clay and Bridport Sands. Uncomformably overlying Cretaceous sands (Albian) form the top of the Beacon.

Plate 6

A. The cliff top at the west end of Burton Cliff showing downfaulted Fuller's Earth Clay (Bathonian) overlying thin limestones of the Inferior Oolite (Bajocian) with vertical cliffs of Bridport Sand (mostly Toarcian) below.

B. Close-up showing the transition from the Bridport Sand to the Inferior Oolite and the condensation of rhythmicity.

C. The lower cliff of Bridport Sand showing unusual evidence for storm deposition indicated by large-scale cross bedding and a shoal structure.

Plate 7

A. Bridport Sands at Burton Cliff showing unconsolidated sands, often showing bedding, and consolidated, well-cemented and heavily-burrowed harder beds.

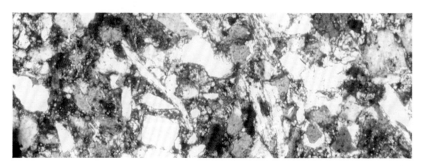

B. Thin section of an unconsolidated level in the Bridport Sands showing angular quartz clasts in a matrix of carbonate and interstitial clay. Note the buckled mica flakes which have been interpreted as evidence of compaction. About ×120.

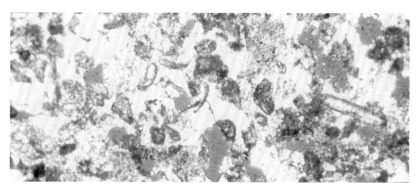

C. Thin section of the Top Beds, Inferior Oolite (Bajocian) from the Burton Bradstock Lane section. This organo-detrital limestone shows well-degraded clasts often etched and coated. About ×30.

Plate 8

A. Fallen blocks of Inferior Oolite at the west end of Burton Cliffs showing the Snuff Box level.

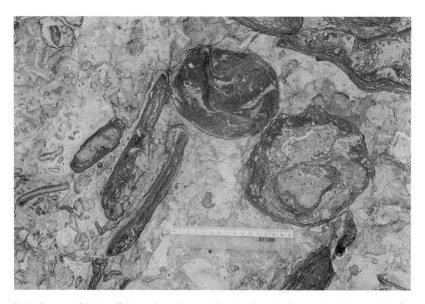

B. A close-up of the Snuff Boxes from the same locality showing the complex history with often several stages of stromatolitic coating of growing clasts.

Plate 9

A. The Bridport Sands below Burton Villas with the downthrown Fuller's Earth Clay in the foreground which are separated from the Bridport Sands by the Bride Fault.

B. A fallen block of Inferior Oolite at the northern end of Burton Cliffs with a metre scale.

C. Surface of a flatstone of Forest Marble from the Fleet shore at Moonfleet Hotel showing abundant organic detritus. ×1.0.

Plate 10

A. The 'Bagshot Beds' at the Hardy Monument above Portesham.

B. The Fleet and Chesil Beach west of Langton Herring showing an old lime kiln on the dip slope of the Cornbrash.

Plate 11

A. West Wear Cliff, Portland, looking north toward Chesil. The white Portland Stone forms the vertical cliff at the top but the Freestone series has been quarried away. The West Wear Sandstones form the dark bluffs below with the *Exogyra* Bed forming the light band in the middle.

B. A complete section through the Portland Stone and overlying Purbeck Beds at Freshwater Bay, Portland. The Cherty Series forms the lower cliff and the Basal Shell Bed and underlying Portland Clay forms the base of the cliff.

Plate 12

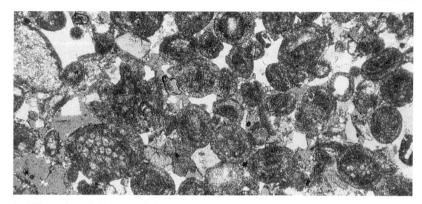

A. Thin section of the Portland Stone, 1.3m below the top, from Freshwater Bay, Portland. About ×30.

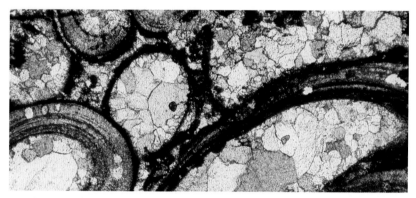

B. Thin section of the Basal Shell Bed, Freshwater Bay, Portland, mostly of serpulid worm tubes in cross section. About ×30.

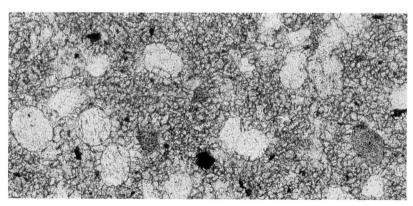

C. Thin section showing rhaxellid sponge spicules in impure silty dolomite from doggers just below the Blacknor Sandstone at Tar Rocks, Portland. About ×30.

Plate 13

B. Giant perisphinctid ammonties from the Portland Freestone. From a former garden museum most of the ammonites from which are now incorporated in the walls of the Portland Heights Hotel.

Plate 14

A. Bowleaze Cove from north of Redcliff Point. The further cliffs show the Upper Oxford Clay and overlying Nothe Grit of the basal Corallian Beds which crops out in the foreground. The blocks show spectacular trace fossils.

B. View from Osmington Mills with the Ham Cliff anticline in the distance approximately aligning with the crest of the Ringstead anticline which passes through the reefs of Corallian Beds in the foreground.

Plate 15

A. View from Osmington Mills towards Bran Point at very low water. The falls in the foreground are over the Preston Grit which also forms the first reef. The gap corresponds to the eroded Nothe Clay and the next reef is due to the basal bed of the Bencliff Grit. Bencliff Grit, with oil-bearing sands at the top, forms the low cliff near the wreck.

B. The Corallian Beds just west of Bran Point, Osmington Mills. The Qualicosta Bed (Bed 2) is the white limestone forming the top of the lowest bench with the top of the Bencliff Grit at the base. Bed 6 is the discrete white band above. Orange Trigonia Beds are at the cliff top.

Plate 16

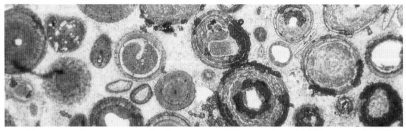

A. Thin section of Osmington Oolite from Arkell's Bed 6 west of Bran Point, showing ooliths, some compound, with various centres, including a snail and quartz grains set in a sparite matrix. About ×30.

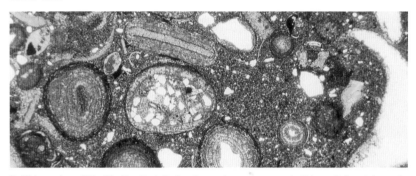

B. Thin section of The Pisolite (Bed 4) showing various centres to pisoliths and clay-rich matrix. About ×15.

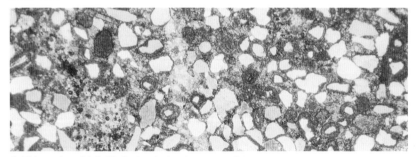

C. Thin section of Arkell's Bed 1, the basal member of the Osmington Oolite, showing abundant of angular quartz grains often as nuclei to incipient ooliths. About ×30.

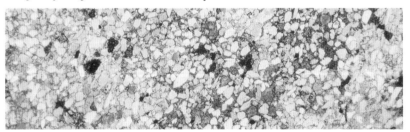

D. Thin section of the Bencliff Grit west of Bran Point showing fine angular quartz grains and carbonate matrix. About ×30.

Plate 17

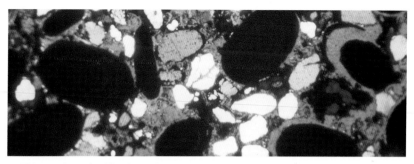

A. Thin section of Abbotsbury Ironstone, Jubilee Coppice, Abbotsbury, showing large ferruginous ooliths and angular quartz sand grains set in a fine-grained matrix. About ×30.

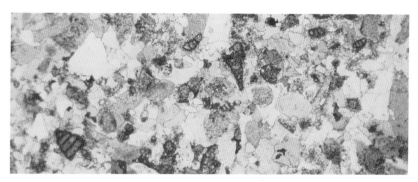

B. Thin section of Upper Greensand from Durdle Cove showing large angular quartz grains, foraminiferans, and occasional rounded clasts of green glauconite. About ×10.

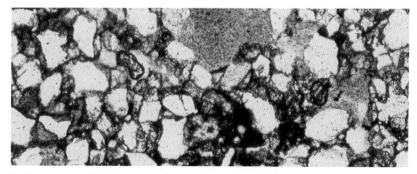

C. Thin section of Wealden ferruginous grit from Durdle Cover, showing angular quartz fragments and amorphous chloritic clasts set in a ferruginous matrix. About ×30.

Plate 18

A. The profile of White Nothe from Bran Point. The Upper Greesand and Gault dips southward across the distant cliff and at the point the top of the Upper Greensand is at sea level. At the west (left) end Portland and Purbeck Beds beneath the unconformity dip north. The near cliff shows Osmington Oolite (below) and the orange Trigonia Beds above.

B. Telephoto showing the unconformable relations between the Portland and Purbeck Beds (below) and the Upper Cretaceous rocks (above) near Holworth House.

C. The Middle White Limestone, Osmington Oolite, at Bran Point showing the U-shaped burrows of *Arenicolites variabilis*.

Plate 19

A. Durdle Door, Durdle Cove and Swyre Head and Bat's Head in the distance.

B. Man-o'-War Cove with a succession from Portland and Purbeck Beds on the left (terminated by a fault where the steps come down), the Wealden Beds and, at Man-o'-War Head northward dipping Middle Chalk faulted against Upper Chalk.

C. Lone Cove, west of Bat's Head, showing the sharply folded foresyncline of the Purbeck fold and vertical to overturned Chalk of Bat's head;

Plate 20

A. The Lulworth Crumple at Stair Hole, Lulworth.

B. The section on the west side of Stair Hole with the Portland Stone forming the massive lower cliffs.

Plate 21

A. View of Lulworth Cove from the east side.

B. Telephoto showing steeply dipping Upper Greensand and an old kiln close to the café at the entrance of Lulworth Cove from the road.

Plate 22

A. The Fossil Forest on the east side of Lulworth Cove. Two vertical tree bases and one collapsed trunk engulfed in stromatolitic limestones.

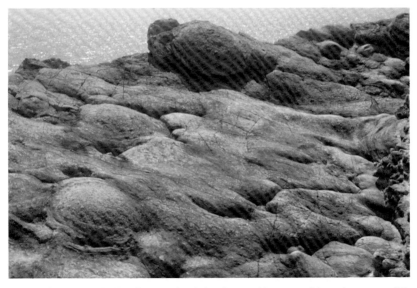

B. A surface above the Fossil Forest level showing a wide cover of irregular stromatolitic limestone.

Plate 23

A. View of Mupe Rocks with a fine section of the Purbeck Beds, and across Worbarrow Bay to Gad Cliff and Kimmeridge.

B. Cross section of the Purbeck fold on the east side of Worbarrow Bay near Arish Mell. A fine section mostly not accessible.

Plate 24

Kimmeridge Bay looking west toward Broad Bench showing the polygonal thrust units developed on the Flats Stone Band and thought to be due to expansion on dolomitisation.

Plate 25

A. The nodding donkey pumping oil from the Kimmeridge Well, just northwest of Gaulter's Gap, Kimmeridge.

B. View across Kimmeridge Bay to the oil well site and beyond to Gad Cliff. The reef strips correspond to stone bands and harder kerogen-rich bands in the shale.

Plate 26

A. Clavell's Hard, Kimmeridge. The bench has an adit into the Kimmeridge Oil Shale (Blackstone) reddened by combustion. A descent can be made from the cliff-top path and, more hazardously to the foreground ledges which are the *Saccocoma*-bearing shales below the Blackstone.

B. Three stone bands descending the cliff below Swyre Head. These are the White Stone Band (below), the Middle Stone Band and the Freshwater Steps Stone Band (above).

C. The White Stone Band at White Lias Rocks below Swyre Head.

Plate 27

A. Thin section of the Blackstone at Clavell's Hard showing crushed palynomorphs and occasional clasts. About ×30.

B. Stereoscan photo of coccoliths in the Rope Lake Head Stone Band at Clavell's Hard. Width of photo 32μm.

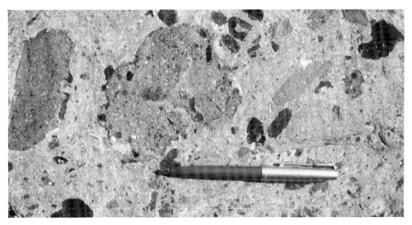

C. Penecontemporaneous conglomerate in the White Stone Band at White Lias Rocks with lignite and mud flakes.

Plate 28

A. Chapman's Pool, Hounstout and the cliffs westward towards Clavell's Hard.

B. A working quarry in the Portland Beds near Pier Bottom, St Alban's Head. Paving stones of Purbeck Beds being prepared for the reflooring of Portsmouth Cathedral.

Plate 29

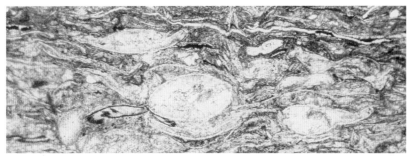

A. Thin section of ostracod limestone, above the Cinder Bed, Durston Bay, Swanage. About ×30.

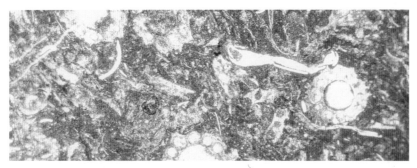

B. Thin section of *Chara* limestone, from near Peveril Point, Durlston Bay, Swanage. About ×30.

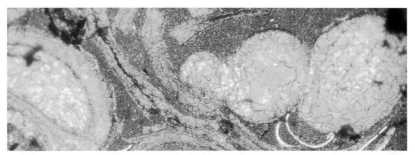

C. Thin section of the Purbeck Marble, from Peveril Point, Swanage. Showing spar-filled gastropods. About ×30.

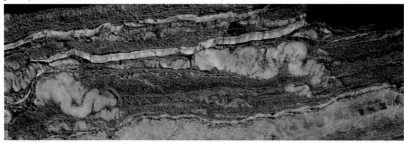

D. Contorted gypsum beds in the Purbeck Beds on the west side of Worbarrow Tout. Each is 1–2 metres in length.

Plate 30

A. St. Alban's Head from the sea.

B. The lighthouse near Tilly Whim Caves, south of Swanage, from the sea.

C. The section of the Portland and Purbeck Beds below Durlston Head.

D. Durlston Bay, before the landslips associated wth the Zig-Zag Path Faults had been contained, at great expense, to preserve the flats of Purbeck Heights.

Plate 31

A. The Ridgeway, along the hog's back of vertical chalk near Creechbarrow showing the quarry near Cucknowle.

B. Corfe Castle from east of Kingston Matravers.

C. The Ballard Down Fault below Ballard Down (Hardfast Point) from a drawing by Thomas Webster in 1815.

Plate 32

A. Hengistbury Head from near Southbourne.

B. South side of Hengistbury Head with the Boscombe Sands below and Barton Clay (Hengistbury Beds) above.